Tolley's
Guide to Employee Rehabilitation

by

Val Hughes
Mike Appleby
Lynda A C Macdonald
Dr Leslie Hawkins
Jenny Chapman
Fiona Stewart

Members of the LexisNexis Group worldwide

United Kingdom	LexisNexis UK, a Division of Reed Elsevier (UK) Ltd, 2 Addiscombe Road, CROYDON CR9 5AF
Argentina	LexisNexis Argentina, BUENOS AIRES
Australia	LexisNexis Butterworths, CHATSWOOD, New South Wales
Austria	LexisNexis Verlag ARD Orac GmbH & Co KG, VIENNA
Canada	LexisNexis Butterworths, MARKHAM, Ontario
Chile	LexisNexis Chile Ltda, SANTIAGO DE CHILE
Czech Republic	Nakladatelství Orac sro, PRAGUE
France	Editions du Juris-Classeur SA, PARIS
Germany	LexisNexis Deutschland GmbH, FRANKFURT and MUNSTER
Hong Kong	LexisNexis Butterworths, HONG KONG
Hungary	HVG-Orac, BUDAPEST
India	LexisNexis Butterworths, NEW DELHI
Ireland	LexisNexis, DUBLIN
Italy	Giuffrè Editore, MILAN
Malaysia	Malayan Law Journal Sdn Bhd, KUALA LUMPUR
New Zealand	LexisNexis Butterworths, WELLINGTON
Poland	Wydawnictwo Prawnicze LexisNexis, WARSAW
Singapore	LexisNexis Butterworths, SINGAPORE
South Africa	LexisNexis Butterworths, DURBAN
Switzerland	Stämpfli Verlag AG, BERNE
USA	LexisNexis, DAYTON, Ohio

© Reed Elsevier (UK) Ltd 2004

Published by LexisNexis UK

A CIP Catalogue record for this book is available from the British Library.

ISBN 0 75452 4698

Typeset by Columns Design Ltd, Reading, UK
Printed and bound in Great Britain by Hobbs the Printers Ltd, Totton, Hampshire

Visit LexisNexis UK at www.lexisnexis.co.uk

About the Authors

Fiona Stewart MBA

Fiona is an experienced strategic business and information management consultant with a strong record of significant successes in a range of public sector organisations and government business enterprises. With over ten years senior management experience in both State and Commonwealth government, particularly in health, community service and workers' compensation/rehabilitation, Fiona has provided leadership in the development of organisational capability in particular related to innovative approaches to customer interaction and service delivery, with particular focus on the health sector and remote and rural communities. Fiona holds a Masters in Business qualification and has worked in the rehabilitation and worker compensation field for ten years.

Jenny Chapman BA (Hons) MCIPD PG Dip PG Cert Adv Dip

Jenny is an independent practitioner, consultant and lecturer in vocational rehabilitation, and has extensive experience of rehabilitation, training and service management in Australia and the UK. Her work as a senior partner of the Rehabilitation Network includes extensive customer and employer liaison concerning both individual rehabilitation programmes and organisational service provision: staff recruitment, mentoring and training; and systems development. Jenny holds a Post Graduate Diploma in Health Promotion, is a Member of the Chartered Institute of Personnel and Development and the Staff and Educational Development Association and has worked in the rehabilitation field for more than 20 years. She is currently a Trustee and Membership Secretary of the National Vocational Rehabilitation Association.

Lynda A C Macdonald MA FCIPD LLM

Lynda is a self-employed, freelance employment law trainer, advisor and writer. For fifteen years prior to starting her own business she gained substantial practical experience of employee relations, recruitment and selection, dismissal procedures, employment law and other aspects of human resource management through working in industry. With this solid background in human resource management, she successfully established, and currently runs, her own business in employment law and management training/consultancy. She is also appointed as a panel member of the Employment Tribunal Service in Aberdeen, where she lives.

Lynda is a university graduate in language and a Fellow of the Chartered Institute of Personnel and Development. Additionally, she has an LLM degree in employment law.

Lynda has to date written nine books on various aspects of employment law, all of which have been published by well-known national publishers.

Contact Lynda at: lyndamacdonald.clara.co.uk
Website: www.lyndamacdonald.co.uk

Mike Appleby Solicitor

Mike is a solicitor who joined Fisher Scoggins LLP as a member in 2003 to concentrate on representing companies and individuals in relation to health and safety and manslaughter prosecutions. Prior to this he was head of health and safety at the national law firm of Thompsons. He is the co-editor of *Corporate Liability: Work Related Deaths and Criminal Prosecutions* (LexisNexis, 2003) and the joint author of the legal chapter in *Tolley's Handbook of Disaster and Emergency Management: Principles and Practice* (2nd edition, 2004). He frequently writes and lectures on health and safety issues and writes a regular column for a leading health and safety magazine.

Leslie Hawkins BSc PhD CBiol MIBiol MOISH

Leslie trained as a clinical physiologist at St Bartholomew's Hospital in London, where he worked until he moved to the University of Surrey in 1970 as lecturer and then senior lecturer in human biology. His research interests at Bart's concerned the pathophysiology of chronic carbon monoxide exposure, which developed into a more general interest in environmental physiology after he joined the University of Surrey. In 1984 he was appointed to the Robens Institute to establish and head an occupational health unit. This has now become the Robens Centre for Occupational Health and Safety. Leslie now holds a professorial grade post as University Director and Director of the Robens Centre. The Robens Centre undertakes consultancy and provides occupational health and safety services and runs post-graduate diploma and masters level courses in occupational health, occupational health nursing, hygiene and safety. He is the University Vice-Chancellor's special advisor on occupational and environmental health. His research and consultancy interests are mainly concerned with the health effects of environmental factors including light, electromagnetic radiation and air pollution. He is a consultant to a number of companies and government bodies on environmental and occupational health issues and on the management of health and safety at work. He is Law Society listed as an expert witness in the fields of health and safety and is involved in both civil litigation and public inquiry cases.

Val Hughes BSc (Hons) PG Dip OHSM MIOSH RGN

Val started her nursing career 20 years ago at Gwynedd General Hospital, North Wales and went on to specialise in ophthalmic nursing at Manchester Royal Eye Hospital. Val continued her ophthalmic nursing career in London and worked at both Moorefield's Eye Hospital and St Thomas' Hospital.

In 1994 she decided to leave ward nursing and went on to qualify and specialise in occupational health nursing. Since then, she has gained a wealth of knowledge, skill and experience in both the private and public sector. Her experiences have ranged from local government in that of councils, NHS, Metropolitan Police Service, retail, financial centres and manufacturing of paints, cars and printing.

She became a Member of the Institute of Occupational Safety and Health in 1997 and more recently successfully completed a Masters degree in Occupational Health and Safety Management at the Middlesex University.

Having lived in London for the past 15 years, last year she relocated to the North East and has been working as an Occupational Health Nurse Manager for an occupational health service provider.

Foreword

Managing Employee Rehabilitation is an innovative book on an important topic as the Office of National Statistics state that over the past 30 years, self-reported, long-standing illness has increased. They class long-standing illness as one that limits daily activities and therefore includes the ability to work. This book begins by outlining of the role of rehabilitation and occupational health (OH). An important feature of this book is that it will explore and integrate the government targets and the part being played by the Department of Work and Pensions, the Health and Safety Executive with the many other government initiatives aimed at helping to get people off benefit and back to work. However, and even more importantly, at the core of the book is the well-being of the individual employee.

Legal compliance and attendance management are often regarded as solely human resources (HR) issues, but OH plays a key role in the rehabilitation of employees with long-standing illness and injury, and the prevention of such situations. This book sets out exactly where each discipline stands with regards to sickness absence and attendance management and is written by those experts practising in the field of OH using evidence-based material. It uses cases studies, which will be worked through, to illustrate the practical aspects of absence management and rehabilitation.

Finding one's way around legislation is not always easy and with the *Disability Discrimination Act 1995* in force both HR and OH need key texts to refer to for evidence-based advice and support and this book provides them with a vital resource. It will also be useful for students of OH and HR who need literature to support their academic and professional development. However prevention is better than cure, so says Dr Leslie Hawkins as he concludes the book highlighting the cyclical nature of OH.

Greta Thornbory TD MSc RGN OHNC DipNOH PGCEA MIOSH

June 2004

Contents

Contents

Table of Cases

Table of Statutes

Table of Statutory Instruments

Table of European Legislation

Chapter 1
Managing Employee Rehabilitation

Introduction   1.1

The text of *Tolley's Guide to Employee Rehabilitation* has been based on the occupational experience of several nursing, medical and legal professionals, along with the most recent evidence based practice currently held in the field of occupational health practice.

This publication has been designed to provide practical advice and guidance to assist human resource managers, line managers, legal advisers and all health and safety professionals, along with newly qualified occupational health nurses to manage or assist in the management of attendance and employee rehabilitation within the workplace, and to help those responsible to meet their legal obligations under health and safety law.

Given the broad subject area, the text is restricted mainly to matters that are likely to be met in the day-to-day work of the busy manager, whom responsibilities over managing attendance arise.

Employee Health   1.2

Health is commonly defined 'as a state of complete physical, mental and social well being, and not merely the absence of disease or infirmity' (World Health Organisation, 1946).

When concerned with employee health it is fundamental to view it holistically, and not merely to view it from a negative perspective in that of absence of ill health (that of diseases) and injury. Incorporating a more positive dimension on health comprising wellbeing and fitness that balances physical, mental and social aspects of health is essential. Wellbeing in the main is concerned with feelings of happiness by the individual and an element of a 'good life' being lived, where physical fitness is the ability to carry out ordinary, everyday tasks without undue physical discomfort or pain.

It is therefore important when professionals are concerned with the education, promotion and management of employee health, that the overall goal is to enhance the balance of physical, mental and social components of positive health coupled with the prevention of physical, mental and social ill health.

1

The workplace can be the source of many ill health problems encountered by people, who are or have been employed there. It is for this reason that the workplace has a valuable role to play in the promotion of health and education that touch on issues of both occupational and general health.

The need for facilities within the workplace to meet health demands, additional to the community based services, that takes a broad approach to health promotion and the prevention of ill health and injury in the work force is what is known today as occupational health services.

What is Occupational Health? 1.3

Work and health are central to all our lives. People who work have specific health care needs and for this reason occupational health services supports individuals and management in identifying and minimising the detrimental effects of health on work and work on health.

As early as 1950 the aims of occupational health was defined by World Health Organisation as 'the promotion and maintenance of the highest degree of physical, mental and social wellbeing of workers in all occupations by preventing departures from health, controlling risk and by the adaptation of work to people and people to their jobs' (International Labour Organisation/World Health Organisation, (1950) cited Harrington, J M, Gill, F S, Aw, T C and Gardiner K, *Occupational Health*, 4th Edition, Blackwell Science, Oxford, 1998). Occupational health has evolved significantly since then in response to the demands of the work environment; having developed from a first aid and general treatment based service, to a growing and comprehensive multi-disciplinary service working for the development of organisations, work environment and more importantly, the worker's health.

Occupational health (OH) is concerned with the effects of the working environment on the health of the worker and the influence of the workers' health status on their ability to perform their duties for which they have been employed to do.

Expansion of occupational health has been greatly assisted by legislation and the medical profession. The *Health and Safety at Work etc. Act 1974* was responsible for imposing comprehensive legal duties on employers and creating a framework for the participation of workers and their representatives in promoting both health and safety, whilst the medical profession has applied the distinction between occupational and non-occupational diseases. Such a distinction has resulted in increased occupational health services, in particular screening within industries, enabling employers to fulfil areas of their responsibility in relation to workers' health.

The ultimate objective of any occupational health service is the protection and promotion of workers' health; however, society, business and economic environments through new technologies, globalisation, fragmented work contracts and an increasing ageing workforce are some examples of new challenges facing occupational health services. The development of infrastructures in both content and provision of services has had to change in order to meet these new demands.

The complexity of the workplace today necessitates that occupational health does not work in isolation. It is therefore important that organisations view the delivery of occupational health as a collaborative initiative between management, health care professionals and health and safety practitioners, and that the services adopted are appropriate to the organisations' corporate goals and culture.

Why Rehabilitate Employees Back into the Workplace?   1.4

Although prevention of ill health and injury is often seen as the priority for organisations, the impact of OH contribution alone in reducing total disability cost to an organisation through improved functional capacity and reduction in long-term sickness absenteeism through rehabilitative programmes is widely acknowledged.

There are many ways of managing sickness absence depending on the nature, type of illness and prognosis for a full recovery. In cases where an employee has been on long-term sickness absence and is expected to return to work, it may be helpful to consider a graduated and structured return to work.

Such an approach may include:

- a reduction in the hours worked each day or week;
- working from home;
- working on specific projects which are not too lengthy or complex;
- job modifications; or
- carrying out partial duties.

Getting the employee back to work in this way is both beneficial to the employee as well as management. As an organisation you will be spending less of your time dealing with the sickness absence problem and you may be able to avoid spending money on employing temporary staff that would otherwise be covering the post. It also makes good business sense to integrate back into the work place those people with the greatest experience and skills in a positive way. Occupational health is a support service that can, when used effectively, help an organisation move towards a more productive partnership between employers and employees.

Benefits to the Employer   1.5

The benefits of occupational health involvement in managing employee attendance and rehabilitation allows management to have access to impartial and objective advice that will enable them, along with their human resource policies, to provide a consistent and fair approach to employee case management. Through occupational health input, management within organisations will benefit from an increased awareness and improved control over sickness absence. Management will be provided with appropriate advice on employee capability to work that will assist in identifying those with genuine health problems. This will allow appropriate early intervention and swift referral to internal agencies by occupational health practitioners that will hopefully result in a quicker return to work with less likelihood of secondary problems.

Additionally, employees will identify with the organisation as a caring employer, which hopefully will improve morale.

From a financial perspective occupational health can assist in reducing both the direct costs of employee wages, and the indirect cost which is frequently not monitored and measured by organisations. Some indirect costs that can be saved by the employer include:

- payment of compensation to injured workers and benefits paid to absentees;
- contractual penalties;
- loss of output;
- overtime payment for replacement employees;
- legal costs;
- cost of fines or other penalties;
- training and supervision of inexperienced replacement employees;
- cost of investigation and potential loss of production;
- administrative costs of managing absence and rescheduling work;
- cost of disruption to the business; and
- increased insurance premiums.

Benefits to the Employee   1.6

The benefits to employees are that they have time to recover while still attending work, and can regain their confidence while being integrated back into the working environment with appropriate support. Any rehabilitative approach works best if the employee feels involved and can see the benefits in returning to work on this graduated basis. Therefore any programme would ideally be discussed some weeks before the return to work, as this would enable any working practices to be amended and the return to work to be planned effectively.

Targets of Securing Health Together 1.7

Whilst there is no statutory requirement for occupational health services, there is a statutory requirement under the *Health and Safety at Work etc. Act 1974* for employers to ensure the health, safety and welfare of its employees. More recent are government initiatives including Securing Health Together ('Securing Health Together – A long term occupational health strategy for England, Scotland and Wales', Health and Safety Commission, HSE Books, London, 2000) and Revitalising Health and Safety ('Revitalising Health and Safety Strategy Statement', Department of the Environment, Transport and the Regions, Health and Safety Commission, HSE Books, London, 2000); as well as government alterations in payment of statutory sick pay (SSP) which allow businesses to take greater accountability over sickness absence management.

Through working in partnership with multiple agencies, the British government, through their occupational health strategy in Securing Health Together (HSC, 2000), proposes that by 2010 there will be:

- a 30 per cent reduction in the number of workdays lost due to work related ill health;

- a 20 per cent reduction in the incidence of work related ill health;

- a 20 per cent reduction in ill health to members of the public caused by work activity;

- everyone currently in employment but off work due to ill health or disability is, where necessary and appropriate, made aware of the opportunities for rehabilitation back into work as early as possible; and

- everyone currently not in employment due to ill health or disability is, where necessary and appropriate, made aware of and offered opportunities to prepare for and find work.

The targets set are designed to focus and inspire action by organisations. The plan is that organisations will set their own targets appropriate to their organisation's needs and associated health concerns.

In order to achieve these targets, five key programmes of work in table 1 below have been forwarded for implementation.

Table 1: Five key programmes of work forwarded for implementation

Compliance	It is anticipated that greater compliance to existing and future legislation relating to occupational health and safety is held by employers. Areas prioritised are: improving current legislation, increasing the involvement of health and safety representatives as well as increasing awareness to employers of *(cont')*

	health and safety law, and the consequences of breaches in legislation through increased fines and sentences.
Continuous improvement	Anticipated is that a more collaborative approach to occupational health and safety is undertaken that involves the joint involvement, innovation, and continuous improvement of the employer, local government agencies, health authorities and local businesses in health initiatives and policy development, which will assist in rehabilitating individuals back to work after ill health.
Knowledge	Proposed is that through improved data collection (monitoring and measuring tools, and co-ordinated research projects), better information can be attained of occupational ill health and injury trends. This will increase the knowledge required to move forward other strategies.
Skills	It is proposed that all health professionals and other interested parties involved in employee health are competent and hold the appropriate skills to carry out their role effectively. This will involve identifying and agreeing the skills required for the individual role, increasing the opportunity for training and raising the awareness of these opportunities.
Support mechanisms	This will entail identifying and setting up frameworks for the delivery of information, advice and support for individuals involved in the strategy, and raising the awareness of these facilities, as well as existing frameworks and how to access them.

Sickness absence – causes of sickness absence   1.8

Reviewing many of the literatures on sickness absence shows that a number of models and theories are proposed as to the cause of sickness absence. Much absence is attributed to medical reasons; in particular long-term absence being the result of musculoskeletal problems and stress (HSC, 2000). Whereas short-term absence results frequently from minor illnesses such as colds, flu, stomach upsets and headaches.

While it is recognised that the population is supposedly getting healthier, sickness absence levels remain high on government and business agendas. This indicates that there must be more than a medical perspective to the cause.

Expressed models on sickness absence   1.9

Proposed causes of sickness absence (Briner, 1996) are medical, deviance, withdrawal, economic and cultural models (Briner, R B, *British Medical Journal*, 313, pp874–877, 5 October 1996). A brief explanation is given of their meaning below.

- **Medical model** – the employee is absent from work due to ill health or injury.

- **Deviance model** – the deviance model views absent employees as less committed, lazy and with negative attitudes.

- **Withdrawal model** – the withdrawal model proposes that employees are absent as a way of withdrawing from unpleasant working conditions or work.

- **Economic model** – the economic model proposes that absence is due to employees wishing to do other things with their time.

- **Cultural model** – the cultural model identifies causes of absence within a social context of organisational attitudes and shared norms.

Although there are many literature reviews detailing expressed theories and models on sickness absence, one common feature found is that a combination of geographical, organisational and personal factors all affect sickness absence.

Table 2 summarises some of the factors affecting sickness absence.

Table 2: Factors affecting sickness absence

Geographical/macro level	Organisational	Personal
Climate	Nature of industry	Age
Region	Size	Gender
Social attitudes	Working conditions	Occupational status
Economic climate	Personnel policy	Personality
Unemployment	Labour turnover	Alcohol intake
Pension age	Occupational health provision	Health status
Social insurance system	Job demands	Length of service
Epidemics	Shift patterns	Leisure activities
Health services		Travel/family responsibilities

It can be identified that absence from work is multi-factorial. Illness is therefore a variable feature in actual sickness absence and the most effective schemes in sickness absence management will address several contributory factors. Developing an organisational multi-disciplinary approach, encompassing the involvement of occupational health to support absence management and rehabilitation and management to set the appropriate culture, policies and monitoring systems within are advocated to successfully achieve strategic business goals.

Cost of sickness absence   1.10

Sickness absence costs British industry an estimated £11.6 billion ('Counting the costs', *CBI absence and labour turnover survey*, Confederation of British Industry, 2002 (available from: http://www.cbi.org.uk accessed 10 February 2003). Current figures for 2001–2002 by the Health and Safety Commission estimate that 2.3 million people were found to have suffered an illness which workers believed was either caused or made worse by their job, and 40.2 million working days were lost to injury or illness (Bean S, *Occupational Health*, p4, February 2003 (HSC figures show sickness absence rates are on the rise). Of the days lost due to illness, 13.4 million were attributed to stress, anxiety and depression, and 12.3 million resulting from musculoskeletal disorders.

The cost of annual absence per employee is estimated between £476 and £522, with the average recording of sickness rates per employee at ten days.

The impact to a business in lost production and quality, together with increasing labour costs and potential poor customer satisfaction and relations, requires the control of absenteeism to be high on business agendas. It is imperative to recognise that there is no one single cause for sickness absence, and indeed to view sickness absence from a medical model perspective alone is too simplistic, given its multi-factorial situation.

Tackling sickness absence both effectively and efficiently requires a proactive approach, through management taking the initiative to monitor absence, enabling them to identify organisational trends and early identification of problems. By following this approach, management can develop appropriate policies and procedures, consult with their employees and instigate prompt occupational health intervention.

Promotion of a positive safety culture in reducing sickness absence caused by ill health and injury   1.11

Effective health and safety policies not only contribute to business performance by preventing accidents and ill health, but can be beneficial for both financial and economic reasons. Failure of health and safety management systems led to many known incidents such as the Kings Cross fire, the capsize of the *Herald of Free Enterprise*, the *Piper Alpha* explosion and the Clapham rail disaster to name only a few.

The Health and Safety Executive (HSE, 1997) in 'Successful Health and Safety Management' (HSG 65) guidance identifies key elements to successful health and safety management ('Successful health and safety management HSG 65', Health and Safety Executive, HSE Books, London, 1997). These include:

- policy;

- organising;

- planning and implementation;

- measuring performance;

- reviewing performance; and

- auditing.

The document proposes that for effective health and safety management, there should be comprehensive health and safety policies which set a clear direction for the organisation to follow and where responsibilities to individuals and the environment are met in ways which meet the spirit and direction laid down by the law. This will contribute to business performance not only from a financial perspective, but through demonstrating commitment to continuous improvement and effective risk control that will be beneficial in reducing ill health and injury.

Through effective management structures and arrangements the delivery of the policy will be more effective. To make your health and safety policy effective, it is important to get staff involved and committed and this is referred to as a 'positive safety culture' (HSE, 1997).

HSG 65 discusses activities necessary to promote a positive health and safety culture and have been arranged into four categories as shown below.

Table 3: Four categories to promote health and safety culture

Control	Securing control within the organisation is achieved by allocating responsibilities for policy formulation and development; for planning and reviewing health and safety activities; and for implementation of plans and reporting on performances. In addition, it is important to lead by example, hence it is important that senior managers demonstrate commitment and provide clear direction. Systems will need to be in place to ensure those responsible for health and safety have the necessary authority and competence to make decisions, and have time to commit to health and safety responsibilities. Additionally it is beneficial for employees to be provided with adequate supervision, instruction and guidance to fulfil their roles, and that they are all held accountable over health and safety issues.
Co-operation	This means securing co-operation between individuals, safety representatives and other groups such as contract workers through involving them in policy formulation and

(cont'd)

	development and in planning, implementing, measuring, auditing and reviewing organisational policy; together with attendance at health and safety meetings by staff and their representatives.
Communication	This implies that communication is secured throughout the organisation by means of visible behaviour, written material and by face to face meetings.
Competence	This implies that arrangements are made within the organisation for recruitment and training of staff, to ensure that those individuals undertaking dangerous work or carrying out health and safety responsibilities have the necessary skills, knowledge and experience to carry them out competently, and that advisory support is made available.

Once the policy is set and the arrangements made within the organisation, it is essential to plan its implementation. Planning is identified as a key to ensuring successful implementation of the health and safety policy, and it is here where the organisation sets out objectives, identifies hazards to health, assess those risks and implements standards for performance, so that performance can be measured against them. Setting performance standards in this way, based on risk control that may entail elimination of risks to health through substitution of safer premises, plant or substances, and ensuring safe systems of work for the individual, makes sound economic and business sense. It is here where prudent employers make sound arrangements in relation to total risk management.

Having planned for implementation, it is imperative to organisations in terms of financial, economic, legal and moral implications that performance is measured, so that the organisations identify whether current arrangements are successful or not. Active monitoring will involve proactive initiatives that involve regular inspection of premises and work, and measuring performance against agreed standards. Whereas reactive monitoring will involve the investigating of injuries and cases of occupational illness, as well as property damage and near misses. This will lead to identification of weaknesses or omissions in performance standards where improvements can then be made.

The final key element of successful health and safety management is that of reviewing and auditing activities, and deciding on ways to improve performance. Auditing, particularly when undertaken by external agencies or by a representative within the organisation, complements the monitoring activities undertaken, as this will result in an assessment of whether the policy, organisation and systems in place are actually being effective.

Having identified the key elements of successful health and safety management, we can apply them to attendance management. Effective management of attendance stress the importance of having a robust attendance management policy that defines their roles and responsibilities and employee responsibilities clearly for managers, as well as the interfacing role of occupational health and health and safety departments.

Within the policy, the planning and setting of standards will be set in that of possibly identified short, long-term and intermittent absence and the method employed for its management. Thereafter, arrangements can be made for measuring and monitoring attendance. Through setting up and managing a system of data collection, assessment of trends, measurement of exposures and the incidence of ill health and injury; the economic cost of work related ill health can be measured and identified. Employers can then understand what problems need to be addressed within their organisation and be supported effectively by occupational health departments.

The responsibility of tackling workplace sickness absence lies mainly with senior management and line managers and must be integrated into the quality control and health and safety management systems of an organisation. Organisations should be encouraged to look beyond the purely medical model approach of tackling sickness absence by implementing the procedures below.

1   Maintaining computerised systems to measure and monitor absence, ensuring accurate collection of data on absence and classifying it.

2   Publishing and adhering to sickness absence management policy encompassing the above, enabling sickness absence to be managed fairly and consistently on behalf of the employer and employee.

3   Carrying out return to work interviews following each absence, so that reasons for absence are identified and acted on.

4   Training line managers on attendance management.

5   Ensuring the culture is appropriately supportive and encouraging, with opportunities for rehabilitation programmes wherever possible.

6   Avoiding a situation where the company is seen only to punish sickness absence.

7   Applying sick pay and ill health retirement rules consistently throughout the organisation.

8   Taking account of the *Disability Discrimination Act 1995* where it applies, or preferably being 'disability blind' and adjusting jobs to suit any health problems wherever possible.

9   Designing job content and work groups to enhance responsibility and decision making latitude, while managing career expectations.

10 Ensuring that pre-employment references include a request for sickness absence information and that it is available to occupational health in all cases where there could be a problem.

11 Implementation of a proactive occupational health service which supports management policies through:

(a)   health promotion activities;

(b)   physiotherapy service;

(c)   rehabilitation programmes; and

(d)   stress counselling or Employee Assistance Programme (EAP).

12   Ensuring a positive safety culture through:

(a)   demonstrating commitment and leadership of directors and senior managers;

(b)   ensuring all managers and employees are clear about their role and responsibilities;

(c)   consultation and participation in health and safety by all levels of staff and unions within an organisation;

(d)   effective risk management, so to control and reduce work related injuries and ill health; and

(e)   continual improvement to the physical working environment.

13   Implementing policies that reward attendance, encourage flexible working arrangements, assist with travel and other family friendly initiatives, so to reduce the pressures experienced from work and family life.

14   Developing systems to measure all costs, direct and indirect costs of absence and its impact on quality.

Role of the occupational health nurse advisor (OHNA) in attendance management   1.12

Occupational health nurse advisors can assist managers to address management issues and trends in sickness absence and provide confidential advice and support to the employee suffering from illness or injury.

The advice provided is impartial and confidential in that medical details will not be discussed to the employer and the information provided will be focused on fitness to work/capability.

Since managers are responsible for the management of attendance, employees may be referred to the OHNA where there are frequent short-term absences, prolonged absences due to a long-term illness, or returning to work after an industrial injury.

It is not the function of OHNAs to manage attendance, but to evaluate the reasons, to identify trends and to consider hazards and risks which may not have been identified or adequately controlled.

Each individual is different and the OHNA following consultation with the employee will advise the manager as to:

- confirmation that there is a health problem likely to affect attendance;

- prognosis if relevant;

- if absent, likely date of return to work;

- any residual disability, permanent or temporary, on return;

- whether the employee can be expected to render a regular and efficient service in the future;

- whether the *Disability Discrimination Act 1995* applies;

- any restrictions to duties either on a temporary or permanent basis;

- whether treatment and/or medication is ongoing and likely to affect work;

- performance; and

- any review date.

Following a health assessment the OHNA will advise management on the above as well as provide impartial and confidential advice to the employee on the most appropriate course of action in management of an ill health concern.

Prevention of ill health and injury is the key focus of occupational health, and the OHNA can provide advice to the individual not only on the health issue presented through the management referral, but on several lifestyle issues such as diet, exercise, smoking cessation, sensible drinking and hygiene.

Additionally the OHNA can visit work sites to give specific health and safety advice on occupational health related matters. OHNAs are experts in occupational health. However, if on such visits safety hazards are noted, they will draw them to the manager's attention and recommend a visit from the local health and safety advisor in post. The OHNA will investigate occupational health aspects of accidents at work; liaising as appropriate with HR and local health and safety personnel.

The role of occupational health is advisory, not regulatory or enforcing. Advice can be provided on any work related health matter, as well as interpretation of health and safety legislation and its practical application. This will be further explored in **CHAPTER 3**.

Chapter 2
The Role of Occupational Health in Rehabilitation

Occupational Health and the Occupational Health Services

What is occupational health? 2.1

It has long been known that work and the conditions at work can influence health. An Italian physician, Bernadino Ramazzini, is often regarded as the 'father of occupational medicine'. He published his first book on the diseases of workers in 1700 (*De morbis artificum diatriba*) in which, among many other observations, he noted that 'the maladies of clerks arise from three causes: first, constant sitting; second incessant movement of the hand and always in the same direction; and thirdly the strain on the mind. The incessant driving of the pen over pages causes intense fatigue of the hand and the whole arm because of the continuous strain on the muscles and tendons'. Here he was describing what is recognised today as repetitive strain injury and stress, two very common conditions affecting the modern workforce. It has been known for a very long time that work can affect the health of workers, which was highlighted during the industrial revolution, when conditions in the mines, cotton mills, the iron industry and factories created a huge number of industrial diseases.

Large numbers of workers at that time suffered illnesses such as pneumoconiosis from breathing dust, byssinosis from breathing cotton dust, industrial deafness from the noise at work and many other diseases associated with the conditions of the workplace. In later years, the introduction of new materials that were thought benign, have subsequently become the cause of significant diseases. Asbestos is a good example, where today there are about 1,800 deaths from mesothelioma, around 4,000 deaths from lung cancer and 160 deaths from asbestosis per annum caused by the previous use of asbestos. More recently, the shift in occupational health has moved away from the diseases of heavy industry, to the conditions caused by new technology and a sedentary but pressurised way of work. Over a million people in the United Kingdom now suffer from a work-related musculoskeletal disorder (mainly upper limb disorders and back pain) and a half a million suffer from stress, depression and anxiety, which they attribute to their work.

However, it is also recognised today that not only do the conditions of work affect health, but a person's health may adversely affect the way he or she can work effectively and safely. An employee who suffers a sports injury may then find it very difficult to undertake manual work. A person who suffers stress because of a domestic crisis, may bring that stress to work and work inefficiently or unsafely. Occupational health, therefore, concerns both the effect of work on health and the effect of ill health on work. In considering the involvement of occupational health in the rehabilitation process, it is the effect of a person's health on their ability effectively and safely return to work which is of concern.

Crucially, occupational health practice is as much involved with *prevention* of ill-health at work as it is with dealing with the consequences of illness which have an impact on work. The risk assessment process allows us to anticipate what harm is likely and to which employees or groups of employees. *Primary prevention* aims to introduce control measures, including health surveillance if appropriate, which should reduce the risk of ill health occurring in the first place. An increasingly important role for the occupational health service is to be actively involved in health promotion. The workplace has become an important venue to get across the healthy lifestyle message and to improve public health. Inevitably though, employees will develop illnesses either work-related or not, which will have an adverse effect on their work. *Secondary prevention* aims to minimise the effect of pre-existing medical conditions on work and tries to ensure that any existing ill health, vulnerability or disability is not made worse by work. Rehabilitation involves the return to work following absence for an injury or medical condition and consequently always involves a need to practice secondary prevention. The important roles of prevention are explored more fully in **CHAPTER 7**.

The occupational health service   2.2

Occupational health services exist to promote the health of employees and to safeguard the organisation from the adverse consequences of employee ill health. A good occupational health service should have as it's priority the prevention of illness and injury, and the promotion of good health. An occupational health service can reduce the risk of illness by ensuring that risk assessments fully take account of the health hazards at work and devise and implement controls that minimise the health risk. The occupational health service can, almost uniquely, include in the risk assessment pre-existing medical conditions, which may make an individual more vulnerable to the conditions in their workplace. For example, an employee with an existing back injury will be very much more vulnerable to further injury from lifting and carrying and the risk assessment for the individual should reflect that. Organisations without an occupational health service may not be aware of the vulnerability of individual employees and therefore unable to exercise their extra duty of care (see **2.15** below).

An occupational health service can also aid the process of prevention of work-related illness by undertaking pre-employment health screening. This, if conducted properly, reduces the chances of the organisation recruiting employees who are unfit for the job and alerts the employer to any restrictions which may need to be applied to ensure that the employee is not exposed to any further risk of illness or exacerbation of their condition. The *Disability Discrimination Act 1995*, requires the employer to make reasonable adjustments to the work and to the workplace, so as not to place those with disability at any disadvantage compared with those who do not have such disability (see **2.19** below and **CHAPTER 4**).

All organisations will, from time to time, have employees who are ill, either because if their work or for some reason completely unconnected with work. If the illness is short, infrequent and for reasons obviously unrelated to work, then the occupational health service does not need to be involved. However, in a proportion of cases, the illness is prolonged, or the individual has frequent short-term periods of sickness absence, or the sick notes reveal what appears to a condition that may be related to the person's work. In these cases, the occupational health service can be of invaluable help to the organisation in managing the continued employment of that individual. If the individual has a serious illness the occupational health service will be able to advise on the rehabilitation and return to work (see **2.12** below).

If the illness is such that it appears that the employee is unlikely ever to return to normal working, then the occupational health service can advise on permanent ill health retirement. Sickness absence always costs an organisation money and in some organisations can amount to a significant proportion of the payroll cost. The occupational health service has an important role to play in helping the organisation manage sickness absence. For example, in some cases frequent short-term absence is an indicator of stress at work. The occupational health service's role in investigating the causes of that individual's stress and advising on what needs to be done to ensure a successful return to work, will help to ensure a rapid and successful return to productive working. So important is the role of the occupational health services in managing work-related stress that the judgement in the case of *Sutherland v Hatton [2002] EWCA Civ 76* ruled that if an organisation refers an individual to a counselling or treatment service it is unlikely to be found in breach of duty.

Occupational health services that perform the sort of functions outlined above are 'proactive' services. They anticipate what are the risks to ill health and where and in whom work-related ill health is likely to occur and put in place a range of functions to prevent ill health arising. Clearly, this is the best form of occupational health practice but some services exist as 'reactive' services. They do little to prevent ill health and then, when it arises, attempt to manage the condition and any possible liability that the organisation has exposed itself to. This is sometimes called the sticking plaster approach to occupational health and, whilst it may be the cheapest to administer it is,in the longer term, most certainly not the most cost effective.

Having extolled the virtues of an occupational health service it has to be said that many organisations will not have any form of occupational health provision whatsoever. In the UK there is a very patchy provision of occupational health services with the smallest organisations having very little, if any, occupational health provision, whilst the very largest often have excellent services. Medium-sized organisations will have anything from no provision at all to having a full or part time occupational health professional or will contract in an external occupational health provider.

The Professions Which Contribute to Occupational Health Practice   2.3

Occupational health is a multi-professional practice. The main contributors are:

- occupational physicians;
- occupational health nurses;
- occupational hygienists;
- safety advisors; and
- ergonomists.

In addition, treatment and preventative services are sometimes provided by:

- physiotherapists;
- chiropractors and osteopaths; and
- counsellors.

Occupational physician   2.4

The role of the occupational physician is to undertake medical examinations and to diagnose work-related ill health, to determine the work-related causes of ill health and to advise on the management of health problems which impact on the person's ability to work. Under some regulations there is a requirement for an 'approved' or 'appointed' doctor, (approved or appointed by the Health and Safety Executive), to determine fitness for work and to keep designated workers under medical supervision. Pension funds also often require a doctor to make the decision regarding permanent ill health retirement or admission to pension schemes, although they do not necessarily have to be specialist occupational physicians.

Occupational physicians are doctors who have specialised in occupational medicine. To become a specialist in occupational medicine the doctor must first of all undertake a programme of study and examination to acquire Associateship of the Faculty of Occupational Medicine (AFOM). This qualification is an indication of the doctor's expertise in occupational medicine but they are not regarded as accredited specialists (with consultant status in National Health Service (NHS) terms) until they have gained full membership of the faculty (MFOM). Full members are admitted to the accreditation register held by the faculty. Some doctors also hold an MSc in Occupational Medicine or a Diploma in Industrial Health (DIH). These are academic qualifications in occupational medicine but holders of these qualifications may or may not be accredited specialists. Confirmation of a doctors accreditation can be obtained from:

The Registration Department
The General Medical Council
178 Great Portland Street
London
W1N 6JE
Tel: 020 7915 3630
Fax: 020 7915 3558

Many doctors, including general practitioners (GPs), offer their services to organisations to act as 'company doctors'. Some non-specialist doctors will have made attempts to gain some understanding of occupational health. The Faculty of Occupational Medicine validates a Diploma in Occupational Medicine, but this is a generalist qualification and is not related to the training needed to gain specialist accreditation.

Doctors can have a crucial role to play in rehabilitation by assessing the individuals' capabilities and health problems in relation to the work they do.

Occupational health nurses   2.5

Occupational health nurses (also called occupational health advisors), are qualified nurses who have specialised in occupational health. Experienced occupational health nurses can determine fitness for work by pre-employment health assessment, monitor the health of people who are at risk of ill health (health surveillance), and advise the organisation on health issues relating to individuals such as sickness absence management. Occupational health nurses also usually play a key role in preventing work-related illness and promoting good health among the workforce. Many occupational health nurses are also competent to undertake environmental assessments such as simple measurements of noise, lighting etc, and workstation assessments. (Assessments that are more detailed may have to be referred to an occupational hygienist or ergonomist).

The occupational health nurse is likely to be the key professional advising on the rehabilitation of employees who have had long-term sickness absence and in monitoring their progress on return to work.

Occupational health nurses are registered nurses whose names appear on the statutory register to practice held by the Nursing and Midwifery Council (NMC). In addition, an occupational health nurse will hold a qualification in occupational health, ie Occupational Health Nursing Certificate (OHNC), post-graduate diploma or degree and their names will be recorded on the specialist register of the Nursing and Midwifery Council. Confirmation of a nurse's general registration and their entry to the specialist practitioner register can be made to the:

Registration Department
Nursing and Midwifery Council
23 Portland Place
London
W1B 1PZ
Tel: 020 7333 9333

Many nurses are employed in commercial and industrial settings who are not qualified occupational health nurses. There is no problem with this as long as the responsibilities placed on the nurse do not exceed his or her level of competence. If the needs of the organisation are to provide a reactive service to treat injuries at work or to promote general health and well-being then a qualified general nurse is acceptable. However, occupational health nursing involves recognising the work-relatedness of ill health, determining health risks at work, advising on the management of health risks and advising the organisation on the management of sickness absence. These activities require training and experience, which only the qualified occupational health nurse is likely to have. Similarly, advice on rehabilitation and managing an employee's return to work requires an understanding and experience of the effects that the person's job may have on his condition and the effect that his condition may have on his ability to do the job.

Occupational hygienists   2.6

Occupational hygienists are employed to measure chemical and physical hazards in the workplace. Information on levels of exposure to chemicals, dusts, fumes, noise etc, is often required in order to determine the risks to health. There is also sometimes a statutory need to determine exposure levels and to keep records of individual exposures. Occupational hygienists are also expert in advising on protective equipment such as the suitability of hearing defenders and dust masks.

Occupational hygienists will have obtained a first degree in occupational hygiene or will have qualified in another subject (often chemistry) and then obtained an MSc in Occupational Hygiene. Another route for qualification is to obtain one of the qualifications of the Faculty of Occupational Hygiene. Before the establishment of the Faculty of Occupational Hygiene in January 2003, hygienists may have qualified with a number of examination bodies, BERBOH, BEBOH, IOH, and BIOH).

The occupational hygienist will sometimes be involved in the rehabilitation process by advising on the possible levels of exposure to harmful substances and by giving advice on how best to protect against exposure.

Safety advisors   2.7

Safety advisors, or health and safety practitioners are usually 'generalists' with in-depth knowledge of safety and a working knowledge of occupational health. They should be competent to carry out all general safety duties, including risk assessment and the implementation and management of risk controls. Typically, the safety advisor's role is to ensure that the organisation has a good health and safety policy and that this covers all of the recognised hazards within the organisation. The safety advisor will be instrumental in ensuring that risk assessments are undertaken and kept up-to-date, will devise suitable means for prevention of illness and injury arising out of the risk assessment and will ensure that these controls are properly implemented. Safety advisors are also usually involved with the education and training of employees in safe working practices. Making sure that people understand the hazards to which they are exposed and what controls are in place and how to use them effectively, is not only a legal requirement (*Regulation 13* of the *Management of Health and Safety at Work Regulations 1999 (SI 1999 No 3242)*), but is an extremely important way of ensuring a safe and healthy work environment.

The qualifications and training of safety advisors is not regulated by law, but there are a number of pathways to recognised qualifications. Legally, the important factor is whether the safety advisor is *competent* (*SI 1999 No 3242, Reg 7*). Under the Regulation, a person would be regarded as competent where they have 'sufficient training and experience or knowledge and other qualities' to undertake the duties required of them. The issue of competence applies equally to anyone who is given responsibilities for health and safety matters within the organisation and it is the employer's responsibility to ensure that those entrusted with health and safety duties are competent. Common means of qualification for safety advisors include first degree or masters level specialist degrees in health and safety, BSc (Hons) Occupational Safety and Health or MSc in Occupational Health and Safety, examination by the National Examination Board for Occupational Safety and Health (NEBOSH) (certificate or diploma) and examination by a number of other recognised organisations, such as the British Safety Council and the Royal Society for the Prevention of Accidents (RoSPA).

Those who qualify for corporate membership of the Institution of Occupational Safety and Health (IOSH) will use the letters MIOSH. This gives a good indication to the level of training achieved and can be verified with IOSH. Professional safety advisors will have often, in addition, accumulated evidence of professional practice at a higher level and submitted this to IOSH to gain registered safety practitioner status (RSP).

IOSH can be contacted at:

Institution of Occupational Health and Safety
The Grange
Highfield Drive
Wigston
Leicestershire
LE18 1NN
Tel: 0116 257 3100

Professional recognition can also be achieved through the National Vocational Qualifications route (NVQs).

The safety advisor can play an important role in the rehabilitation process by revising risk assessments on return to work, to take account of any disabilities, vulnerability or limitations the employee may now have which did not apply when the risk assessment was last carried out. The safety advisor can also provide any new or additional information or safety training that may be required.

Ergonomists 2.8

Ergonomists have specialist skills, which enable them to design work systems that optimise the match between the person and their work and work environment. The important skill of the ergonomist is to understand the mental and physical capabilities of people and the wide range of human variability, and to design work systems which impact least on the person's health.

Applying ergonomics principles is particularly valuable in ensuring that physically demanding work does not exceed the limitations of the human body. Determination of safe lifting limits and constraints in posture and frequency in lifting are examples of how ergonomic principles can be applied to reduce the risk of musculoskeletal injury. Another example of good ergonomic practice is in the design of the dimensions and layout of computer workstations so as to limit the risk of eyestrain, headache, neck pain and upper limb disorder. The ergonomist can therefore make an important contribution to the reduction of ill health associated with a number of working environments in which mental or physical load is a significant hazard.

Ergonomists often have backgrounds as psychologists, physiologists, physiotherapists or engineers. Some may have moved into ergonomics by experience, some may have taken a masters (MSc) in ergonomics or health ergonomics. The question of competence is again important as mentioned above. The Ergonomics Society has a list of members but this is not a guarantee of competence in a particular field of ergonomics.

The Ergonomics Society
Devonshire House
Devonshire Square
Loughborough
LE11 3DN
Tel: 01509 234904

Physiotherapists   2.9

Physiotherapists can play an important part in the rehabilitation process. Physiotherapists are trained to treat disorders of the musculoskeletal system by a variety of manipulative and physical methods. Physiotherapy is available on the NHS and the individual's GP may have organised a course of treatment as part of the medical management of the person's condition. However, it is sometimes very cost effective for the employer to arrange and pay privately for physiotherapy in order to speed up the return to work or to speed the rehabilitation process once the person has returned. It is unusual for organisations to employ directly a physiotherapist but it is usually possible to find a practitioner who will come to the workplace. Whilst this may be cost effective if there are a number of employees who can benefit from physiotherapy treatment, for the individual employee who may need a course of physiotherapy to aid the return to full working capacity, referral to a private physiotherapy practice is the more cost effective option. Some physiotherapists specialise in occupational health and these practitioners use their understanding of the work and the workplace to help rehabilitate a person back to a specific job. Physiotherapists who specialise in the workplace are often also qualified in ergonomics. Physiotherapists who specialise in occupational health are usually members of the Association of Chartered Physiotherapists in Occupational Health and Ergonomics (ACPOHE).

The Chartered Society of Physiotherapists has a website on which private physiotherapists in all areas can be located, and if someone with occupational health experience is required this needs to be specified (see www.csp.org.uk/physio2u.cfm).

Chiropractors and osteopaths 2.10

Chiropractors use different manipulative techniques but have the same aim as physiotherapists in treating musculoskeletal disorders. Chiropractors also claim to treat some organic disorders (eg migraine) by chiropractic techniques. Some chiropractors are now specifically aiming their services towards workplace treatment and prevention. Osteopaths also use different techniques from both chiropractors and physiotherapists but again claim much success in treating a range of musculoskeletal disorders.

Chiropractors and osteopaths are now regulated by law. Chiropractic is regulated by the *Chiropractors Act 1994*. To practice as a chiropractor, the practitioner must be registered with the General Chiropractic Council (GCC). A chiropractor's registration can be checked on the GCC's website at: www.gcc-uk.org or by emailing registrations@gcc-uk.org. It is also possible to locate a registered chiropractor in your area on the GCC website.

Osteopaths are regulated by the *Osteopaths Act 1993*. It is a criminal offence to describe yourself as an osteopath unless you are on the statutory register held by the General Osteopathic Council (GOC). You can check whether a practitioner is on the National Osteopathic Database and locate a registered practitioner in your area on the GOC website at: www.osteopathonline.com.

Counsellors 2.11

A number of organisations allow employees to be seen by a counsellor. This may be a one-off arrangement in response to an employee's problem or may be part of an EAP available to staff at any time. Talking to a trained counsellor can be a very successful way of helping a person through a period of emotional crisis and can prevent that person losing time through sickness or can speed up the return to work. Many organisations consider that there are considerable cost benefits in paying for counselling, where it is appropriate to do so. Some organisation co-ordinate referral to a counsellor through the occupational health service. In that way the individual's confidentiality can be maintained, the occupational health advisor can advise on whether counselling is the most appropriate treatment, and can keep a check on the number of counselling sessions the person is having and how well the individual is responding. The occupational health advisor can also help select the counsellor or psychotherapist with the most appropriate experience for that person's needs. This can be very important as counsellors vary widely in their qualifications and experience and in the types of counselling and psychotherapy in which they specialise.

Counsellors are not regulated by law but do have standards of professional conduct through professional bodies. A good guide to the professional training and competence of counsellors is to check if they are accredited by the British Association of Counselling and Psychotherapy (BACP). Accredited counsellors (together with details of their training and special interests), can be located for your area on the BACP website at: www.bacp.co.uk.

The Role of Occupational Health in the Rehabilitation of Employees

Assessment of the individual 2.12

Too often an employee will return to work after a prolonged period of sickness absence without an assessment of what the return will mean for the individual or for the organisation. A possible scenario here, for example, is a person who has been away for six months with depression and anxiety apparently caused by stress at work. The individual indicates to the personnel department that they want to return to work and personnel inform the person's line manager that he or she will be returning on a certain date. On return, the person immediately feels out of depth because a lot has changed in the six months they have been away. They try to get back into the job they were doing, but the pressures that were there before are still there and before long they are ill again and have to go off sick.

No preparation was made for the return to work. The personnel department took it at face value that the person was fit to return to work and no attempt was made to ensure that the person was not exposed to the same pressures that caused the original illness. Cases such as these expose the organisation to civil litigation for damages for breach of duty of care. There may also a case to be made that by not taking into account a known disability on return to work, that this breaches the *Disability Discrimination Act 1995* (see **CHAPTER 4**). It is imperative therefore, that before a person returns to work after any prolonged or serious illness, injury or surgery that an assessment is made both of the individual and the consequences of the return to work.

In most cases, an occupational health advisor can make the assessment. In some cases where there are complicated medical issues or where the prognosis for recovery is uncertain it may be also be necessary to obtain the opinion of an occupational physician. The purpose of the assessment is to obtain a clear picture of the individual's illness, the stage of recovery they are now at, the prognosis for further recovery, and what residual incapacity there may be. It is very important also, to have full understanding of the person's job, what risk assessments are in place which apply to that job, (ie what hazards they have in their working environment and how these are controlled) and other issues which may be relevant. These will include the support the individual can get from colleagues, and what flexibility there is in the job (can the person work from home for some of the time or work flexible hours, for example?).

Information on the job and the work environment can, of course, be obtained from within the organisation, it is simply a matter of collating it from various sources, but information on the person's medical condition has to be obtained from the GP or from the specialist treating the person. The personnel department can itself write to obtain a medical opinion from the GP (with the individual's informed consent). However, the request should be limited to non-clinically confidential information. Best practice and a more informed judgement on the person's current state of health and any residual health problems that may impact on work, is best obtained by a health professional such as an occupational health advisor.

Obtaining medical records   2.13

It is sometimes necessary to obtain the medical records of an employee who has been on prolonged sickness absence and who now intends to return to work, in order to make a judgement about the current state of the person's health. If this is done then it is important that these are obtained by a heath professional employed by the company (or engaged by the company under contract) who can take responsibility for the confidentiality of the records. Medical records should always be kept confidentially under the guardianship of a registered medical practitioner or registered nurse, and should not form part of the person's personnel file.

Often, however, it is unnecessary to obtain the full medical records and for the purpose of determining the fitness to return to work it is sufficient to obtain a medical report from the person's GP or specialist (or both). When requesting a report from the person's physician it is important to say what the purpose of the report is. If the doctor knows that a report is for the purpose of determining how and when their patient can return to work they can word it in such a way as to be most helpful to the organisation. However, it has to be remembered that a GP or hospital doctor is unlikely to know any more about a person's job than simply what he does for a living. Translating the report into a plan for return to work will require a detailed knowledge of the job, job hazards, the flexibilities allowed for in the job and the reasons for the illness occurring if it is work-related. Only an occupational health advisor with detailed knowledge of the organisation and the job the person does can properly make these judgements.

Requesting medical records or a medical report requires the informed consent of the individual and is subject to the legal requirement of the *Access to Medical Reports Act 1988 (AMRA 1988)* (in the case of medical *reports*) and the *Data Protection Act 1998 (DPA 1998)* (in the case of health and medical *records*). The right of personal access to health records used to be under the *Access to Health Records Act 1990*, but this has now been repealed by *DPA 1998*. The only provision now contained in the *Access to Health Records Act 1999 (AHRA 1990)* is where access is requested to health records pertaining to the deceased. Under *AMRA 1988*, an individual has the right of access to any medical report relating to him or her which is to be, or has been, supplied by a medical practitioner for employment purposes or insurance purposes. The Act requires that anyone seeking a medical report on an individual must first of all notify the person that he intends to request a medical report and secondly, must obtain the consent of the individual on whom the report is to be written. When notifying the person of an intention to request a report, the person must be informed of his or her right to withhold consent. They must also be informed of another right under the Act, which is to be able to see the report before it is issued to their employer. The person may ask to see a copy of the report at any time up to 21 days from the application for the report being made to a doctor (but can also apply to the medical practitioner at any time in the following six months for access to it). Doctors cannot, therefore, release a medical report for 21 days after the request has been made, in case the individual asks to see it before being released to the employer. If a person asks to see a report before 21 days has elapsed, they may then make an application to the doctor to amend the report if they believe it to be misleading or inaccurate.

Subject access to health records under *DPA 1998* is much wider than under *AMRA 1988*. It applies to any health record kept by any health professional including doctors, nurses, midwives, dentists, chiropodists, physiotherapists and clinical psychologists, who are, or have been, responsible for the care of the individual. An applicant for access to a health record can be the patient or another person that the patient has authorised in writing to make application on their behalf. In the case of an employer seeking access to an employee's health records, the employer is acting on behalf of the patient (his employee) and therefore must seek written informed consent to make an application. Under this Act, the individual does not have the automatic right to see the record before it is released to the applicant, but does have the right to subsequently request that any misleading or inaccurate entry in the health records is corrected.

The normal way in which an employer seeks to obtain a medical report or access to health records is to explain to the employee what the purpose is in requesting a medical report or copies of health records and asking the employee to sign a consent form. The consent form must clearly spell out the legal rights of the individual under *AMRA 1988* and *DPA 1998*. An example of a consent form to obtain a medical report is shown in figure 1 below.

Knowledge of the individual's job   2.14

In assessing a person's fitness to return to work, it is imperative that the job the person does and the work environment in which they will return to work, is taken fully into account. Take the scenario of an employee who has been off sick for four months with a back injury sustained lifting a heavy pallet of goods onto the back of a lorry. The individual is a warehouseman whose job is to collect items from storage to make up customer orders and to load these onto the back of delivery vehicles. The report from the GP says that the person has made a good recovery and that there is no reason why he cannot return to work. However, the GP has made this comment without detailed knowledge of the individual's job such as the weight of the loads he carries and the height he lifts them, or the fact that the loading of the lorry is done outdoors in inclement weather. The occupational health advisor is therefore in a much better position to translate the medical opinion that the individual is now medically fit, to a judgement as to how fit that person is to do the job. Medical fitness and fitness to work are often very different.

The starting point in this example is to make sure that the person's job has been assessed under the provisions of the *Manual Handling Operations Regulations 1992 (SI 1992 No 2793)* and the revised guidance of 1998. If it has, then a comparison must be made between what are the safe limits for lifting that were determined by

Figure 1: Example consent form to obtain a medical report

UniS

Please complete in black and capital letters:	University of Surrey, Guildford, Surrey GU2 7XH, UK	European Institute of Health & Medical Sciences

The Robens Centre for Occupational Health and Safety
4 Heavhy Road
The Surrey Research Park
Guildford
Surrey, GU2 7RE, UK
Telephone +44 (0)1483 879690
Facsimile +44 (0)1483 876691
Email rcohs@surrey.ac.uk

First Name:

Surname:

Date of Birth:

Job Title:

Home Address:

CONSENT FOR THE DISCLOSURE OF MEDICAL INFORMATION

I consent to the Robens Centre for Occupational Health applying for a medical report from my medical practitioner/specialist* I wish/do not wish* to have access to the report before it is supplied.
* Delete as appropriate

Medical Practitioner's/Specialist's* name:

Address:

I understand that the clinical details in this report will be treated in professional confidence by the Occupational Health Service. Advice based on the report may be given to concerned management. I have read the summary of rights under the Access to Medical Reports Act 1988 as set out overleaf

Signature   Date

Page 1 of 2

ACCESS TO MEDICAL REPORTS ACT 1988

The purpose of this Act is to establish a right of access by individuals to reports relating to themselves provided by medical practitioners for employment or insurance purposes. The Access to Medical Reports Act applies to medical practitioners who are or have been responsible for your clinical care.

Your rights under this Act:

1. You can withhold your consent to the making of a medical report. (However a decision regarding your employment can be made without it and may not be to your advantage.)

2. You can ask to see the report before it is received by the requesting party.

   You can either inform the requesting party who will inform your medical practitioner or

   You can inform your medical practitioner directly within 21 days of being notified that an application is being made.

   If you wish to see the report please contact your GP as soon as possible to avoid any unnecessary delays. In any case the report will be sent off after 21 days.

   You have a right to see any medical report relating to you which has been provided for employment or insurance purposes which has been written in the last 6 months.

3. Before giving consent for the report to be sent off you may ask your medical practitioner in writing to amend anything you think is incorrect or misleading. If the medical practitioner does not agree, a statement of your views will be attached to the report if you request it.

4. The medical practitioner is not obliged to give you access to any part of the report if he/she believes that it would seriously harm your health or others or if it reveals information about another person who has provided the doctor with information about you.

If you require further guidance with respect to the provision of the Access to Medical Reports Act 1988 please contact your Occupational Health Adviser at the Robens Centre for Occupational Health.

the risk assessment and what the employee was doing in practice. It may be that despite the risk assessment the employee was lifting unsafe loads in an unsafe way which contributed to his back injury. If that is the case, then the conclusions of the risk assessment must be re-emphasised to the employee and any additional or refreshment training in safe lifting technique should be given. The possibility that unsafe lifting was occurring may also need to be brought to the attention of the supervisor whose job it should be to make sure that loads are kept below the limits specified in the risk assessment, that, if appropriate, lifting is shared by two people, or that lifting aids are available and used. It may be the case that the legally required risk assessment had not been carried out, in which case the occupational health adviser or safety advisor should ensure that this is done before the person returns to work. The occupational health adviser or safety advisor should also take into account the necessity for outdoor working. Very cold weather or wet weather can increase the risk from lifting, and if not already done so, must be taken into account in the risk assessment.

The experienced occupational health advisor or safety advisor will also know that anyone who has had a back injury, especially one that necessitated four months sick leave, is likely to be more vulnerable to back injury in the future. It is therefore important to ensure that on return to work any additional factors such as a new susceptibility to back injury is taken into account in a revised risk assessment. This may mean that additional safeguards are put in place to minimise the risk of further injury to that individual.

The successful rehabilitation of this individual back to their old job therefore requires much more than a medical assessment that they are now fit to return to work. It requires a complete reassessment of the job, and the risk assessments that go that with job, to make sure that when the person returns to work that they are not exposed to the same risks that caused the original injury. Someone can only successfully do this if they have a close understanding of the person, their medical condition, the job they do and the environment in which they do it.

Risk assessments 2.15

The rehabilitation process often requires any risk assessments that relate to the individual returning to work to be revisited. The example above shows how important this can be in the case of a risk assessment made under the *Manual Handling Operations Regulations 1992 (SI 1992 No 2793)*. This applies equally to almost any risk assessment. The important consideration is that a risk assessment that relates to an individual's job should take into account any personal characteristics of the individual such as sex, height, age or existing disabilities, limitations of capability or existing illness, which may have a bearing on the outcome of the risk assessment. An example is a risk assessment carried out under the *Control of Substances Hazardous to Health Regulations 2002 (SI 2002 No 2677)*, on a substance that is known to cause dermatitis. Clearly there is a risk of sensitisation in anyone which has to be controlled, but someone in whom a sensitisation to that substance has already occurred will need far greater risk controls, or indeed may not be able to work with that substance at all. The principle here is the common law principle of extra duty of care. This was laid down in the judgment of *Paris v Stepney Borough Council [1951] All ER*. In this case, Mr Paris had been blinded in one eye during the war, a fact which, at first, he had concealed from his employer. However, this came to light when he was examined by a doctor for the council's superannuation scheme, at which point he was given two weeks' notice of dismissal. Two days before he was due to leave he was using a hammer on a U-bolt on a truck he was repairing when a piece of metal flew off into his good eye, blinding him. He claimed damages saying that, as he was extra susceptible of serious injury, he should have been provided with goggles. The House of Lords upheld his claim. This created the legal precedent that if an employer is aware that an employee has a vulnerability, then they owe that person an extra duty of care. That is to say, that efforts over and above those considered reasonable for the majority of employees will have to be made in order not to put that person at additional risk. This is a common law duty and any redress will only come if that extra duty is not applied and the person subsequently suffers additional ill health or injury. In that case, they may have a strong case if they bring a claim for damages. In some ways this is similar to the efforts which may have to be made to rehabilitate someone back into the workplace under the statutory duty imposed by the *Disability Discrimination Act 1995 (DDA 1995)*, although that only applies if the person is returning to work with a disability (under the meaning of the Act) which they did not have before their sickness absence. There are very good reasons, therefore, for any risk assessments that relate to the individual's job to be revisited before the person returns to work. It is also a good opportunity to ensure that all of the relevant risk assessments, which should have been done, as they apply to that persons job, have in fact been done.

The occupational health advisor often plays an important role in contributing to the reassessment of risks. They may make the reassessment themselves or may work closely with the safety advisor. The important contribution that occupational health makes to the reassessment, is the understanding that the occupational health advisor has of the person's medical condition and the physical, physiological or mental limitations that they may have when they return to work. The occupational health advisor will also know, from the medical reports obtained, what the prognosis is and whether any limitations are temporary or likely to be permanent. Temporary limitations on capability can be treated in a different way, by for example phasing a return to work or restricting the job in some way so as reduce the risk until the person's recovery is complete. Temporary limitations do not require reasonable adjustments to be made under *DDA 1995*. Long-term limitations will need to be accommodated permanently into the job and the risk assessment, and may even necessitate decisions as to whether the person can continue to do the job they used to do. The occupational health advisor is likely also to want to keep the person returning to work under surveillance until it is reasonable to assume that rehabilitation is complete (see **2.18** below).

Advice to managers   2.16

The role of occupational health is always advisory. The occupational health service can make professional judgements about the fitness of a person to return to work, when they will be fit to return and any restrictions on that person's ability to work which be imposed by the recent illness or injury from which they are recovering. This advice is conveyed to managers but ultimately it is the manager's responsibility to manage the return to work, taking into account the job that has to be done, the practicality of the advice being given and possibly the financial implications of that advice. Good occupational health advisors will communicate fully with managers before any advice is given and will, as far as possible, take into account the operational factors that concern the manager. However, the occupational health advisor has to make a judgement based on the medical condition of the employee, advice given by his or her doctors and the wishes of the employee. This advice is sometimes in conflict with the operational demands placed on the manager.

For example, a teacher has been off sick with stress for five months. The stress was caused mainly by a breakdown in her marriage and although compounded by her work, the work itself was not the cause. The employee now feels much better, but not fully well, and her doctors have reported that she has responded well to treatment and is much improved. The employee wants to return to work; she feels able to cope again and, an important consideration for her, if she does not return soon her sick pay will be reduced. Occupational health decide that the best way of getting her back to a fully productive work pattern is to phase her return. The suggestion is made that she works two hours a day for the first month, increasing this to half a day for the next month and then, hopefully, a full return to work. Occupational health would monitor her during this rehabilitation period. However, the head teacher considers that this is unacceptable. His position is that either she is fit to resume work or she is not, and that he cannot plan to cover lessons with his teacher working part time and variable hours. Neither can he be sure that the teacher will not cope and go off sick again.

A phased return is often a useful means of easing someone back into a fully productive working environment. In some occupations like nursing, medicine, teaching, social work and in organisations with few employees, managing a phased return can be difficult. However, managers do have to consider the implications of not doing what is reasonably practical to organise a phased return to work, even though for a time it may be disruptive, it may cost money and it may be difficult to plan. If the manager insists that the person returns immediately to full working (especially against the advice of occupational health) then there is a very real risk of successful litigation, should the employee's health be made worse as a result. If the manager insists that the employee cannot return unless he or she is fully fit to resume work, then that too may adversely affect the employee's health. The individual may additionally be stressed by a reduction in pay, and the longer a person is away from work the more difficult it is to return. Insistence on full fitness before returning to work may result ultimately in ill health retirement. In all of these types of scenario, the employer has also to bear in mind the requirement of the *Disability Discrimination Act 1995*, which may, if any impairment is both substantial and likely to have a long-term impact on ability, pose an overriding legal duty to ensure that reasonable adjustments are made for a return to work. If a phased return is considered to be a reasonable adjustment then it has to be arranged. The employer would have to have very strong grounds for arguing (perhaps in an industrial tribunal) that a phased return was unreasonable.

A phased return is only one option for rehabilitation, other options are discussed more fully in **CHAPTER 3**.

Confidentiality 2.17

Occupational health professionals work to a strict code of professional conduct which includes a client's right to confidentiality. This often creates conflict in occupational health practice, when a manager wants to know more about an employee's medical condition than the occupational health doctor or nurse can reveal. Generally, the advice given to managers is that a person is fit for work, or is unfit, or that certain restrictions should apply when that person returns to the workplace. The reason for the person's sickness absence may of course be common knowledge, but that does not allow the doctor or nurse to divulge any more about the employee's health than is already known by the manager. Exceptions to this are when the employee gives informed consent for the employer to be told about a medical condition. It may be in the best interests of the employee for the employer to know about a medical condition. For example if an employee develops unstable diabetes it would be in his or her best interest for the employer to know that they may become unwell at work and what to do in those circumstances. In such cases, occupational health would advise the employee to let it be known what their problem is. As another example, an employee may be returning to work following an extensive absence for a brain injury but has now been left with a tendency to epilepsy. In this case, depending on the person's job, they may not only be putting themselves in danger but other people. In most cases a responsible employee would not want to withhold such information but if they did not give their consent the occupational health doctor or nurse could decide that there is an overriding concern for the safety of others and divulge a confidentiality.

Monitoring the return to work 2.18

An important role for occupational health is to monitor the return to work. *Regulation 6* of the *Management of Health and Safety at Work Regulations 1999 (SI 1999 No 3242)*, imposes a legal duty to ensure that employees are provided with such health surveillance as is appropriate. The Approved Code of Practice recognises a number of criteria which should apply in deciding when health surveillance is appropriate:

- where there is an identifiable disease or adverse health outcome related to the work concerned;

- where valid techniques exists to detect indications of the disease or condition;

- where there is a reasonable likelihood that the disease or condition may occur under the particular conditions of work; and

- where surveillance is likely to further protect the health of the employee to be covered.

In the case of an employee returning to work after a period of prolonged sickness absence for a work-related cause, these criteria are usually met and health surveillance is therefore a legal requirement. However, the form of the surveillance should be tailored to the particular condition of the employee and the type of work and the work environment to which they are returning. Someone who has been off with a broken ankle who is returning to a sedentary office job, can be asked simply to report any difficulty they encounter to occupational heath, in a sense self-surveillance. Someone returning to an typing job after an operation for carpal tunnel syndrome (a form of work-related upper limb disorder), will need to be kept under close health surveillance for several months after return to work to ensure that there is no return of the symptoms or development of other symptoms of upper limb disorder. Even after the monitored return to work period, an employee with a history of upper limb disorder should be encouraged to self report any symptoms of recurrence of the condition.

Occupational Health and the Disability Discrimination Act 1995   2.19

It is not the purpose of this section to describe the *Disability Discrimination Act 1995* and its requirements. This is fully explained in **CHAPTER 4**. This section deals with the role that occupational health can play in the process of ensuring compliance with the Act.

Advising when the DDA 1995 will apply   2.20

Occupational health is often in the position of advising managers of the implications of the *Disability Discrimination Act 1995 (DDA 1995)*. Many organisations use a pre-employment health assessment or self-completed health declaration to determine a person's fitness for the job for which they are being recruited. Since the Act applies at the point of recruitment as well as during employment, occupational health has to advise managers if, at the time of recruitment, a disability within the meaning of the Act, has to be taken into account when employing that person. For example a person has applied for a job as a porter, but the pre-employment assessment reveals the he has rheumatoid arthritis. The Act defines a disability as both being substantial and having a long-term adverse effect on the ability to carry out day-to-day activities, so this person would come within the meaning of the Act. It can be justified to treat that person less favourably than others who apply for the job if the disability affects their functional performance to the extent that they cannot perform the demands of the job.

The occupational health advisor therefore has to know two things in order to advise managers appropriately. What is the functional ability of the applicant and what are the demands of the job? Both of these factors are difficult to determine in absolute terms, so professional judgements have to made, and perhaps, at a later date, have to be defended. Functional capacity can be judged by an understanding of the applicant's medical history; the seriousness of the condition at present and how well they are responding to treatment. Does the person currently do a similar job and what is their sickness absence record for their arthritis? The demands of the job have to be judged against the loads expected to be moved, the heights to which they may have to be lifted, the frequency with which lifting and carrying forms part of the job, the usual posture in which lifting may occur and the environment in which the work is carried out. The manual handling elements of the job should have been assessed under the *Manual Handling Operations Regulations 1992 (SI 1992 No 2793)*, and this would form part of the information available to the occupational health advisor or physician in making a judgement. With this information to hand the employer can be advised in one of three ways that:

- the applicant is fit for the job;

- the job would need to be modified in certain (specified) respects to make it non-discriminatory to the applicant; or

- the person is unfit for the job.

If the decision is made that adjustments have to made to the job so that the applicant is not treated any less favourably than any other applicant, then the occupational health advisor or physician must be specific about what aspects of the job would need to be modified or where it might be appropriate to provide equipment such as lifting or carrying aids. This requires occupational health staff to have a good understanding of the job and what modifications would be feasible and reasonable. Nothing does more to undermine the credibility of an occupational health service, than for the occupational health advice to lack an appreciation of the realities of the job and the needs of the organisation.

What applies at pre-employment can apply equally when a person is returning to work after a period of prolonged sickness absence. The *DDA 1995* applies in the same way if an employee develops a disability that they did not have at some earlier stage in their employment. The functional capacity of the employee may now be impaired compared with his capacity before the illness or injury. The occupational health advisor needs again to form a view about the individual's functional impairment and relate this to the demands of the job. However, for an existing employee another option arises which does not apply to someone being recruited for a job. In this case the *DDA 1995* requires the possibility to be investigated for re-deployment to another job, which can accommodate any newly acquired disability. The options available to the occupational health advisor or physician are now; fit to return to work, fit to return but with specified restrictions, fit to return provided specified adjustments are made to the work or workplace, and unfit for the current job but potentially fit for other employment within the organisation. Again, this last advice must be made by the occupational health advisor with a full understanding of the feasibility of re-deployment within the organisation.

Advising what adjustments can be made 2.21

The occupational health advisor or physician should play an important role in help-ing to determine what adjustments can be made to accommodate a person's newly acquired disability. However, the occupational health team has to work closely with managers in determining what is practical and hence what is reasonable. The law only requires adjustments which are *reasonable*. The occupational health team's con-tribution is to understand the human factors involved and the individual's medical condition, whilst the manager has the understanding of what is feasible within the workplace and within the constraints of operational requirements. What is a *reason-able* has to be interpreted within the context of the job and the organisation. What might be reasonable for a large organisation may be unreasonable for a small busi-ness with limited resources. A decision that the necessary adjustments are *unreason-able*, must always be made with the thought in mind that such as decision may have to be defended under cross examination in an industrial tribunal.

Ergonomists can play an important role in helping to design the necessary adjust-ments to the work or workplace in order to accommodate a newly acquired dis-ability (see **2.8** above). The ergonomist has an understanding of human factors and the range of human capacities. The principles of ergonomics can be used to design the way work is organised as well as the physical aspects of the work envi-ronment to take account of any reduced capacity or limitation of an individual. Ergonomics is sometimes defined as a 'user centred approach to design' and this is it's importance in determining what adjustments can be made to ensure that someone is able to continue working without discrimination. Redesigning the work, workplace or work equipment may be a crucial way of making the reason-able adjustments required under the *Disability Discrimination Act 1995*.

Case studies 2.22

The way in which adjustments can be made are best illustrated by brief case stud-ies. One illustrates what can be done in the case of a rehabilitation from a mental illness and one from a physical illness.

A case of depression 2.23

Case study I

Mrs X was a married woman in her early 50's who had worked for the same organisation as an accounts clerk for 20 years. The company had not changed its working practices much in that time and Mrs X was settled in a job with which she was very familiar and coped with easily. When the company was taken over by a larger company this equilibrium was dramatically changed. Mrs X, like her colleagues, was now subject to a different and more demand-ing management style in which targets were set and performance was mea-sured. A new computer system and new software applications were installed with which the staff were unfamiliar. The younger members of staff responded well to the training provided and soon adapted to the new way of working, but Mrs X was not so adaptable. She could not cope with the new technology, was feeling left behind by her younger colleagues and was frequently arguing with her manager who was unsympathetic with her lack of skills in the new system. She began feeling unwell and started taking days off. Her doctor diagnosed stress and she was signed off sick. Her inability to work made her depressed and she was prescribed antidepressants.

After several months of sickness absence and treatment, her doctor felt she was well enough to consider going back to work. The company's occupational health advisor was asked to advise on Mrs X's return to work. An assessment of the case quickly revealed that nothing had changed in the job which made Mrs X ill in the first place. Whilst her depression was much improved it was a reactive depression which was very likely to be reactivated by a return to the work which had made her ill. The occupational health advisor discussed the options with Mrs X before advising her line manager that Mrs X was fit to return to work but not in the capacity she had previously been deployed. The occupational health advisor enquired with HR to see if there were vacancies elsewhere in the company to which Mrs X could be redeployed. There was a vacancy in the sales department which suited her abilities and did not require the computer skill that she was lacking. She was therefore offered a new job with no disadvantage to her salary and conditions of service or pension rights. She accepted and soon returned to full health.

Lessons to be learned

- Requiring her to return to the job which had made her ill, which had not changed and to which no reasonable adjustments could be made was very likely to cause her condition to deteriorate. This would have given Mrs X a strong case to bring a claim for damages for the company's failure in its duty of care towards her.

- The *Disability Discrimination Act 1995* applies to mental disability as well as to physical disability. In this case her susceptibility to depression can be regarded as a disability under the Act and the employer has a duty to make reasonable adjustments to the work on her return.

- It was not reasonable to change the working practices, which Mrs X could not cope with, but the Act also requires the possibility of redeployment to be considered. In this case, redeployment to another more suited job was the preferred (and successful) option.

An upper limb disorder   2.24

Case study 2

John Y was a 28-year-old data entry clerk. His work involved intensive key board and mouse work, a job he had been doing for five years. He started to develop numbness and tingling in his right arm which he reported to his manager. His manager did nothing. After a few months the pain become so bad that he took days off to recover. His self-certificated sick notes mentioned pain in the arm but these went to the personnel department who did not alert the department manager. After several more weeks the pain was chronic and he went to his doctor who diagnosed repetitive strain injury and prescribed pain killers and referred him for physiotherapy. He also signed him off sick. After several weeks he was improved and wanted to return to work. By this time the occupational health service had been notified of his condition and informed of his intention to return to work. The occupational health advisor asked to see the risk assessment done under the *Health and Safety (Display Screen Equipment) Regulations 1992 (SI 1992 No 2792)* There was none. The advice was therefore given to management that there should be a risk assessment done under the Regulations but as John now had a recognisable upper limb disorder, then a full ergonomic appraisal of his work and workstation should be made before he could return to work. The occupational health service therefore engaged an ergonomist and worked with him to undertake a full assessment of John's work and workstation. John returned for a morning to explain to the ergonomist how he worked and how he sat at his workstation. The ergonomist's report highlighted a number of faults in the way John worked, in the lack of training he had been given, how he set up his workstation and in the intensity and pacing of the work he was given. As a result advice was given on what new equipment should be provided (a wrist rest and different type of mouse and as it was mainly numerical data entry, a numerical keypad), and what training should be given so that John could make optimal adjustments to his workstation. In addition, advice was given that the volume of work should be reduced and adequate rest pauses should be built into the day. A proper risk assessment was recorded. The occupational health advisor advised John's manager that he could return to work once these recommendations were adopted and that she was going to keep John under health surveillance.

Lessons to be learned

- The company should have heeded early warnings of upper limb disorder. Intervention at an early stage can prevent progression towards a more serious condition.

- If the company has access to an occupational health service make use of it. Make sure managers know when and how to refer and make sure that personnel refer cases which may come to their attention through sick notes. In this case, neither the manager nor personnel acted on early

> warnings that a serious condition was developing. Failure to act can expose the company to claims of negligence.
>
> - If the company does not have access to an occupational health service, make sure some other arrangements are in place to act promptly on early signs of a health problem (for example ask the person's GP to refer privately to a specialist for advice or seek advice from an occupational health service, such as through NHS Plus).).

Areas of Special Concern

Mental health 2.25

Returning to work following periods of illness for a mental health problem represents one of occupational health's most difficult challenges. On the one hand, it is often difficult to assess accurately how well a person really is, even with reports from the individual's physician or psychiatrist. A person who has been off sick with a mental health problem may well have their own agenda for returning to work and may not be entirely honest about their state of health. Their mental state may prevent them from making rational judgements about their ability to return to work or the medication they are on may give them a distorted perception about their ability to return to work. This means the occupational health advisor or physician has to use all of their experience in cutting through the evidence before them, including interviewing the person, before deciding whether the person is truly fit to return to work or what adjustments may have to be made to ensure a successful return to work.

Fitness to return to work involves a consideration both of the work that the person will be returning to and the possible impact work may have on the health of the individual. It is important to know whether the work or work pressures were in any way causative or contributory to the mental illness the person had suffered. A period of absence may have taken the pressure off and the person's health improved as a result. However, returning to the same job with the same pressures would be very likely to result in a further deterioration in health. The longer a person has been absent for a mental health problem the more difficult it usually is for them to return to work without considerable support. It is also often daunting for someone to come back to work with colleagues who will probably know why the person has been away. Many see stress as a weakness and even if their colleagues are sympathetic and supportive, the person will often feel that have let them down and will feel stigmatised.

Where stress or other forms of common psychological illness such as depression and anxiety are caused by factors unrelated to work, the job of the occupational health advisor is more difficult because there is very little influence that can be exerted in the workplace to ensure that, on return to work, the person will not become ill again. In many cases the pattern of illness is one of recurring periods of sickness absence. Where sickness absence, or performance when at work, is seriously affecting the ability of the person to do their job, consideration may need to be taken for retirement on grounds of ill health. Where the cause of the psychological illness is outside the control of the employer then the *Disability Discrimination Act 1995 (DDA 1995)* may apply but it may be difficult to make reasonable adjustments to resolve the problem. Dismissal or ill health retirement against the wishes of the individual may need to defended.

Assessment of the fitness of the person to return to work not only involves the health of the individual and the likely prognosis, but the also the nature of the job they are expected to do. Post traumatic stress, following a traumatic incident at work, may leave a person unable to undertake a crucial part of their job. An emergency services worker, who was involved in a serious crash whilst driving at speed to an incident, might be unable to drive an emergency vehicle again. A teacher who has had a serious head injury may be left with amnesia and unable to teach their subject. In such cases reasonable adjustment, including redeployment, will need to considered under the *DDA 1995*, but if such adjustment are not considered possible, early retirement may be the only course of action.

Where a person is considered fit to return to work to following a period of sickness for a mental health problem or where they may be returning following an injury or surgery which has created a psychological disorder, then it is usually necessary to monitor their return to work. The occupational health advisor should plan a return-to-work health surveillance under which the person is seen on a regular basis initially with the period between interviews gradually lengthening, depending on the person's progress and any continuing problems. It is important to allow the person to return to full normal working as soon as possible. Someone recovering from a depressive illness may have low self-esteem and lack confidence for a period of time. Long periods of health surveillance may seem to mark the person out as being different from his or her colleagues and impede full recovery. Face-to-face monitoring should be replaced as soon as possible after the return to work, with self monitoring in which the person is assured that support is available but left to seek help for themselves should they feel the need.

Stress   2.26

Stress is usually considered a form of psychological disorder in which the person feels that they cannot cope with the pressures placed upon them. In some case this will be entirely pressures arising from work, in which case the employer has a legal duty of care. In some cases the factors causing stress arise solely from outside of work such a debt burden, relationship difficulties or bereavement. In these cases, the person's stress will usually affect work, and the employer has to manage frequent sickness absence or lack of performance. In many cases, stress has both a work and non-work cause. The pressures that arise from the person's home life can add together with the pressure at work to create a load that the person feels they are unable to bear. The employer has a duty here to ensure that the job is not creating unreasonable pressures, but is not legally liable for factors that are outside of his control. Since stress is a form of psychological disorder, the issues relating to mental health, discussed above will apply. However, stress has some special considerations because of the possibility that the factors causing the ill health arise either wholly or in part from the work and from the civil liability that might ensue if the employer does not exercise a proper duty of care.

An employer has a special responsibility for someone returning to work following a period of absence for stress. The case of *Walker v Northumberland County Council [1995] 1 All ER 737* created a precedent that stress is to be considered just like any other vulnerability and that once a person's stress proneness is known to the employer they owe that person an extra duty of care (see **2.15** above). The legal consideration of course is the one of foreseeability. Where a person has had a period of absence for a diagnosed condition of stress, then the employer cannot argue that the harm which might arise from stress in the workplace was not reasonably foreseeable. Since (1995) the case of *Sutherland v Hatton [2002] EWCA Civ 76* in the Court of Appeal, has set a list of principles which should be applied in claims for damages for stress. These principles include the test of foreseeability what the employer knows (or ought reasonably to know) about the employee's proneness to stress, and that this test applies whatever the occupation (ie there are no jobs which should be regarded as intrinsically dangerous to mental health). Among the 16 principles laid down is also one that an employer who offers a confidential advice service with referral to an appropriate counselling or treatment service is unlikely to be in breach of duty. The *Sutherland v Hatton [2002] EWCA Civ 76* appeal included three other appellants, one of which was Leon Barber appealing against the dismissal of his claim in *Somerset County Council v Barber [2002] EWCA Civ 76*. Barber subsequently took his case to the House of Lords (*Barber v Somerset County Council [2004] UKHL 13 HL(E)*), who have overturned the Court of Appeal decision to dismiss the claim for damages but have broadly endorsed the Court of Appeal's principles. In the House of Lords judgment it was clear that the employer had been made aware of the circumstances of Mr Barber's illness and had failed to make sympathetic enquiries about his state of health on return to work and had failed to take appropriate measures to reduce his workload. These then are becoming the established principles, which should dictate the employers' actions when someone returns to work following a period of absence for stress.

Musculoskeletal disorders   2.27

Musculoskeletal disorders include back injury and upper limb disorders. These may be work-related (caused by the conditions of work) or may be caused by activities outside of work (sports injuries, leisure activities such as DIY or gardening, or arising from accidents such as whiplash). Often minor discomforts arising from musculoskeletal injury are endured and the employee does not have significant time off. The issue of rehabilitation in these circumstances does not arise. However, when the injury or disorder causes significant pain and loss of functional capacity the person may be forced to stop work or may be advised to do so by his or her doctor. It matters very little if the musculoskeletal injury was caused by work or by activities outside of work. When the person returns from a period of sickness absence there needs to be an assessment of whether the injury will be made worse by the job the person does. If it is clearly a work-related injury (such as a work related upper limb disorder) then attention needs to be paid to the work the person was doing, the workstation layout and organisational issues such as rest breaks and stress which may have contributed to the onset of the condition. As with stress (see **2.26** above) the same legal principles apply. That is, if the employer knows that a person has a predisposition, say to back pain, then they have a duty of care to ensure that work does not exacerbate the condition. This applies equally whether or not the condition was caused by work.

Determining someone's fitness to return to work will require an assessment of the job and an assessment of the individual's medical condition. The health assessment will need to include an assessment of the person's functional capacity or limitations in functional ability. For example someone recovering from a back injury may have a limitation on their ability to lift and carry loads. If this type of activity forms any part of the person's job then action must be taken on return to work to ensure that this will not adversely affect recovery and will not cause recurrence of the problem.

Options for reasonable adjustments will depend on the nature of the musculoskeletal disorder and the scope for alteration of the job and way it is done. For example if lifting is only an occasional part of the person's job (lifting computers in an IT role for example), then it will be possible to advise against undertaking this type of activity and alternative arrangements will have to made for someone else (a porter for example) to do the lifting when this is required. If lifting is a significant part of the job it may be necessary to explore ways of reducing manual handling. For example, using lifting aids, insisting on shared lifting of heavy or awkward loads, or reducing individual weights by splitting loads. Where lifting is an essential part of the job (a hospital porter for example) and it would not be reasonable to do the job in a different way then it may be necessary to consider redeployment or even ill health retirement if there are no reasonable adjustments that can be made. Training (or refresher training) in safe lifting techniques will also often form part of the rehabilitation process.

The common work-related musculoskeletal disorders are covered by legislation which requires risk assessments to have been made. Lifting and carrying falls within the *Manual Handling Operations Regulations 1992 (SI 1992 No 2793)* and the revised Guidance (1998), and display screen work comes within the *Health and Safety (Display Screen Equipment) Regulations 1992 (SI 1992 No 2792)* as amended by the *Health and Safety (Miscellaneous Amendment) Regulations 2002 (SI 2002 No 2174)*. Any other activity which gives rise to a risk of musculoskeletal injury has to be assessed under the *Management of Health and Safety at Work Regulations 1999 (SI 1999 No 3242)*. Under any of these regulations a risk assessment should have been made to determine the nature and extent of the risk and to devise and put into practice any remedial actions considered necessary to avert the risk. The fact that someone has been off sick with a work-related musculoskeletal injury suggests that the risk assessment was not done at all or was incomplete or faulty. Before someone returns to work it is important to redo the risk assessment. This time, however, it may be necessary to take into account any functional limitations which the employee may now have which didn't apply at the time of the original assessment. Under *SI 1999 No 3242, Reg 3 (3)* there is a legal obligation to review the risk assessment if there is any reason to believe that it is no longer valid or there has been a significant change in the matters to which it relates.

Rehabilitation following cardiovascular illness   2.28

Cardiovascular illness usually means acute illness, or the long-term consequences, following a heart attack (myocardial infarction) or a stroke. However, rehabilitation to work may follow other serious heart or blood vessel disease such as heart rhythm abnormalities, heart valve surgery or surgical repair of vascular aneurysms.

The important factor in determining fitness to return to work is for the occupational health advisor to have a complete picture of the employee's medical condition, such as:

● what was the medical condition;

● what treatment was received (and importantly may continue to be received after returning to work); and

● what is the prognosis for complete recovery or what residual incapacity may remain?

To gain this information it will be necessary to obtain a report from the GP or from the hospital specialist (see **2.13** above). This information has to be related to the person's job and to what extent the job may affect the person's health or how any residual incapacity may affect ability to do the job (or do it safely). Information on the medical condition will allow a decision on fitness to return and any restrictions to work or rehabilitation options such as phased return over a period of time.

Adjustments may be necessary (including those legally required under the *Disability Discrimination Act 1995* (*DDA 1995*)), in order to facilitate the person's return to work. For example following a heart attack, it may be quite possible for the person to satisfactorily return to a sedentary job but not to return to a job which entails hard physical activity. It may be possible to redesign the job to avoid strenuous work or it may be possible to deploy the person to an office-based job. The job might entail exposure to substances or conditions at work, which may affect cardiovascular function. Examples are exposure to substance such as carbon monoxide (from vehicle exhaust for example), exposure to extremes of heat or cold, or to vibration. Shift work is another factor that may adversely affect a person recovering from cardiovascular illness and it may be necessary to adjust the person's work so that they work only a day shift.

Another consideration is when someone returning to work has been fitted with a cardiac pacemaker or an automatic implantable cardioverter defibrillator (AICD). These devices can be disturbed by strong electromagnetic fields and if the person's job entails possible exposure to magnetic fields (in electrical engineering for example) a risk assessment should be undertaken before the employee returns to the workplace.

41

Chapter 3
What is Rehabilitation?

Introduction to Rehabilitation 3.1

There are many ways of managing sickness absence depending on the nature, type of illness and prognosis for a full recovery. Occupational rehabilitation is the process of assisting an employee back into the workplace following injury or illness, whether it is work related or not. The aim of the rehabilitation programme should be to restore the individual to the highest possible level of functioning as soon as it is appropriate. It allows the employee to regain their confidence and integrates them back into the working environment with appropriate multi-disciplinary support. Early intervention is the most important principle in disability management. As soon as it is medically safe for the employee to return to work, arrangements should be instigated. Using their own worksite for rehabilitation eliminates the disincentives that frequently results from long separation from the workplace.

The rehabilitation process involves early intervention with adequate, appropriate and timely services based on the individual's health needs assessment.

In cases where an employee has been on long-term sickness absence and is expected to return to work, it may be helpful to consider a graduated and structured return to work. Such an approach may include:

- a reduction in the hours worked each day or week;

- working from home;

- working on specific projects which are not too lengthy or complex; or

- carrying out partial duties.

Principles of Rehabilitation 3.2

There are many important principles that should be considered when planning rehabilitation programmes. Firstly, there should be commitment by all parties concerned in the programme, with the primary goal focusing on the maintenance at work or the early return of the individual to work where they have suffered a work injury or disease. Commitment from senior management is paramount and this should not only be with the writing of a corporate policy, but deep seated in the culture of the organisation which is demonstrated through individual behaviour, and importantly, action promoting a positive health and safety culture.

It is important that the employee plays an active, empowered role in the process and that all parties act respectfully to each other, with sensitivity and confidentiality of the employee's health status information to be maintained.

Consultation is critical between employee and employer (and their representative, should it be appropriate) and it is best that any programme is ideally discussed some weeks before the return to work, as this would enable any working practices to be amended and the return to work to be planned effectively. Thereafter, regular, closely monitored review periods should be agreed by both parties and written reports made.

Where possible the programme should aim to return the employee to work in the same job, the same job with reasonable adjustments (having considered the implications of the *Disability Discrimination Act 1995*), or to a new job with the same employer.

It is imperative to consider that no employee suffers any financial disadvantage by participating in a return to work programme and that the work allocated is meaningful to the employee. Any programme of rehabilitation is best implemented with the support of an occupational health service together with health and safety support.

In cases where the organisation chooses to write a rehabilitation policy alongside an attendance management policy, it is considered appropriate that the following be incorporated:

- policy philosophy including aims and objectives – this will demonstrate a commitment to fairness at work for ill, injured individuals or to those with a disability;

- a statement that identifies commitment by all parties and that a partnership is being established, along with a formal structure of the communication strategy to be employed;

- a eligibility criteria and how the injured or disabled employee is to be supported;

- identification of any budgetary and resource commitments;

- identification of available resources, in that of services, professionals to fulfil the services and the systems in place to evaluate the services;

- a statement on confidentiality of medical information and that information held on the employee is stored securely and treated by all parties sensitively and with respect;

- accountabilities held by all parties for successful outcomes; and

- a strategy in place to resolve any disputes should they incur.

The Referral Process for Occupational Health Intervention 3.3

An organisation will primarily aim to promote and maintain a healthy workforce. On occasions, referral to a specialist occupational health practitioner is needed in order to assist with absence management and identification of work related ill health. The HR department and line manager can utilise the support of occupational health to assist with this.

It is usual that a formal paper referral is completed by management when referral to occupational health is required. This type of paper referral is normally designed to ensure that the occupational health team is given full and appropriate background information regarding the concerns held over the employee. This enables occupational health to address these issues with the employee and provide HR or line management with a response which meets their needs.

Advice is provided both to employer and employee. Occupational health can assist managers to address management issues and trends in sickness absence, and provide confidential and impartial advice and support to the employee suffering from illness or injury.

The advice provided is impartial and confidential in that employee medical details will not be discussed to the employer and the information provided will be focused on fitness to work or capability. No personnel external to the occupational health team are given access to an employee's occupational health record unless it is with a written and informed consent of the employee to whom the consent refers.

In some cases further medical information may be sought from the employee's GP or hospital consultant and this is only undertaken with the written consent of the employee concerned.

Circumstances when an occupational health referral is appropriate 3.4

Short-term absence   Employees with frequent short-term absence can be assessed to determine if there is any underlying medical reason to account for their absences, any relevant medical action that can be taken or the likelihood of improved attendance in the future.

Long-term absence   All cases of long-term absence (over two weeks) should be reviewed in order to assess the likely length of absence and to make any rehabilitation recommendations, which may facilitate an early return.

Possible work related   In situations where the work or working environment
ill health   may be affecting employee health and safety, occupational health referral is essential. The aim is to establish
whether there is an occupationally related cause and if
so, advise on measures to minimise or eliminate the
problem.

Types of illnesses and injuries to benefit from early intervention of an occupational health referral   3.5

The following is a general guide to the types of illnesses and injuries which are
likely to benefit from early intervention via an occupational health referral:

- serious medical conditions, eg heart attack, stroke;

- stress, anxiety, depression, fatigue;

- musculoskeletal conditions, eg serious strains or sprains, fractured bones,
back and neck complaints, repetitive strain injuries such as wrist problems;

- any long-term illness or disability, eg Crohn's disease, arthritis;

- work-related illness or injury;

- post-operatively – abdominal surgery, heart surgery, hernia repair;

- cases where there are frequent periods of absence without an identifiable
cause; and

- any period of sickness absence of two or more weeks for any medical condition.

This is not a definitive list and should just be used as a guide. For clarification and
further advice on appropriate referral, it is advised that contact is made with the
occupational health service.

The referral process   3.6

The referral process for occupational health advice is as follows.

1   The line manager should in the first instance, monitor the problem(s),
which may give rise to the reason(s) for referral.

2   The line manager should contact the HR department when advice is
needed. If referral to occupational health is appropriate, the employee will
be seen by HR or line manager to explain the reasons why, and what
advice is being sought. Constraints associated with medical confidentiality
should be acknowledged. Human resources may also instigate a referral in
the same way should they be solely responsible for managing attendance
within the organisation.

3   The referral form is completed and any relevant background information included. This is then forwarded to the occupational health professional under confidential cover.

4   Members of the occupational health team, in most cases the occupational health nurse advisor (OHNA) will then action appropriately.

5   When all enquiries are complete and full information gathered following an assessment with the employee, a report is provided to the line or human resources manager within a mutually agreed timescale following the appointment.

Role of line manager or HR in attendance management 3.7

It is the responsibility of the line manager or HR to manage attendance (sickness absence) and the following information may be helpful in fulfilling this role.

The line manager or HR needs to ensure that a member of staff who is sick contacts them as early as possible on their first day of sickness.

The line manager or HR should establish if support from occupational health is appropriate and if the individual would want to access it. If the individual says no and the manager does not see any need for occupational health involvement at that stage, then they should remain in regular contact (every one to two weeks) with the individual until they return to work. This contact will ensure that the manager is kept up to date on the individual progress, likely date of return to work and also ensures that the individual feels there is support from their manager.

The line manager should refer the individual to the occupational health department (through the management referral form) as soon as possible if the individual goes off sick with an illness or injury where early intervention could speed up their return to work.

Role of the occupational health nurse advisor in attendance management 3.8

On receipt of the management referral form at the occupational health department, the OHNA will make contact with the employee by telephone and assess whether the issue can be dealt with over the telephone or whether a meeting would be more appropriate. The OHNA will use professional knowledge, experience and judgement to decide which is appropriate.

Whichever method of communication is used, the OHNA will attempt to contact the client at the earliest opportunity to arrange an assessment interview or undertake a telephone assessment.

During a health assessment interview with the employee, the OHNA will seek information from the employee to answer management's specific questions. These may include:

- confirmation that there is a health problem likely to affect attendance;
- prognosis if relevant;
- if absent, likely date of return to work;
- obtaining medical information from the individual's GP or consultant, with the person's consent;
- advice on whether there is any residual disability, permanent or temporary, on return to work;
- whether the employee can be expected to render a regular and efficient service in the future;
- whether the *Disability Discrimination Act 1995* applies;
- advice on whether any restrictions to duties, either on a temporary or permanent basis, is necessary;
- advice on appropriate rehabilitation eg physiotherapy;
- advice on whether treatment or medication is ongoing and likely to affect work performance;
- any review date; and
- whether a referral to the occupational health physician, physiotherapy, counselling or any other external specialist may be required.

The OHNA will provide impartial health advice to the individual and thereafter, ongoing support.

The role of the occupational health nurse advisor in recuperative duties 3.9

The OHNA's responsibility is to advise management whether a rehabilitation programme or recuperative duties will assist the employee to return to work. The final decision rests with management.

Where any referral results either immediately or subsequently in the OHNA considering recuperative duties, the employee should be seen wherever possible.

Points to consider by the OHNA in determining Recuperative duties will include:

- reason for length of absence;
- whether the condition is chronic or acute;

- whether the GP or specialist considers the employee fit to return to work;

- whether the employee's medical condition prohibits obvious tasks, eg manual handling;

- current treatments and any need for abstraction for appointments;

- what the employees job entails and what can they do safely;

- whether they are they psychologically fit to return to work;

- access to workplace and method of travel;

- whether travel may make condition worse;

- consideration of how long the individual can comfortably stand or sit for;

- whether they use the stairs;

- whether concentration levels are affected;

- whether home working is an option;

- whether the employee is over eager to return to work due to salary issues; and

- whether the employee is entitled to part payment under the terms and conditions of any disability plan by the organisation's insurers.

If the OHNA wishes to recommend recuperative duties, discussion should be had with management before these are confirmed to the employee. If managers are unable to accommodate recuperative duties the employee will either have to remain off work, or if still at work go off sick.

It is difficult to be precisely prescriptive regarding what hours or exact duties will be appropriate, but generally the following reduced hours are appropriate:

- a minimum of 16 hours per week – this allows for rehabilitation appointments such as physiotherapy or counselling if appropriate;

- a minimum of four hours on any one day – any less is normally neither effective nor operationally acceptable;

- all parties should agree a gradual increase in hours until full duties are possible within a six to eight-week period; and

- the OHNA will assume and advise that any attendance for rehabilitation would be outside the hours to be actually worked.

Following discussion and agreement with management, a confirmation report will be sent to the line manager and HR. Management will be kept informed of progress while the employee is on recuperative duties.

The role of the line manager in recuperative duties   3.10

The initiative to offer a rehabilitation programme lies with management. The manager will need to balance the needs of the individual with the overriding need to provide a high-quality service. The manager in these cases will need to take account of the nature of the illness, the employees working pattern, the effects of these arrangements on other colleagues, and the appropriateness of this approach for the particular service. The decision to operate a rehabilitation programme does not lay with the occupational health service, but with the manager. However, the occupational health service will be a valuable source of information to enable the manager to come to a view.

Where possible the manager will need to be reasonable when, for example, allocating different duties. It would be considered unreasonable to expect an employee to come back on shorter hours to do a job they have no training or experience of undertaking, eg undertaking an administrative role with the use of specific software packages where they have been used to undertaking a manual role such as a being a plumber and where they have little office experience. Particular care is needed when creating a programme for manual workers, as a number of their skills and abilities are not transferable to other environments.

A rehabilitation programme should involve timescales. A clear expectation from the manager, based on advice sought by the occupational health service to the period within which the employee will return to resume their full duties, should be given and agreed at the outset.

Should the programme involve an element of working at home, the manager will then need to be mindful that they are able to manage the situation and allocate and monitor work easily. Additionally, if a computer is used within the home, then a display screen equipment workstation risk assessment will need to be undertaken to meet with legal requirements.

The role of the employee in recuperative duties   3.11

The employee will be the central person in the return to work process. The employee will be responsible for reporting an injury or illness to the supervisor or line manager immediately, and will be responsible in participating in any accident or incident investigation process.

While absent from work the employee has a responsibility to remain in regular contact with the line manager or supervisor and with the occupational health service, should a referral have been made, and provide them with regular health updates as to their progress so to plan for a return to work.

Any rehabilitation programme will work best if the employee feels involved and can see the benefits in returning to work on this graduated basis. Any programme would ideally be discussed some weeks before the return to work, as this would enable any working practices to be amended and the return to work to be planned effectively. It is recommended that in order to avoid any misunderstanding, the line manager confirms any discussion in writing.

The employee will have a responsibility to keep their appointments with all health care professionals and provide health updates to those responsible for their rehabilitation programme.

Risk Management   3.12

There are a number of reasons for managing risk within an organisation, other than compliance with legal requirements, to avoid formal enforcement leading to criminal penalties. Protection of the workforce through appropriate risk control not only leads to a reduction in accidents and ill health, but economically results in reduced direct costs such as fines and insurance premiums, and indirect costs (those often uninsured such as time spent on investigations, agency staff cover, training and legal action). Management of risk will result in better utilisation of plant and equipment, motivation and morale of staff that hopefully leads to higher productivity and efficiency for the company.

Social attitudes have changed towards acceptability and tolerability of risk, with many aspects of life tolerated in the past, such as environmental pollution, being no longer acceptable today. These places an ethical and moral duty on leaders of society involved in public policy and organisations, to ensure that people and the activities they manage do not harm others or their property. Reducing risks to acceptable levels through risk management contributes to business performance by preventing accidents and ill health, and by promoting a positive safety culture. Further, reducing risks to acceptable levels can be conclusively beneficial for ethical, financial and economic reasons, hence risk assessment being a significant element in effective risk management.

Risk Assessment   3.13

Risk assessment involves the careful examination of what could cause harm to an individual in the workplace, so that an employer can weigh up whether they have taken enough precautions or should do more to prevent harm. The aim of undertaking a risk assessment is to identify what hazards are there in the workplace (this may be chemical, electrical, physical or psychological) and determining who might be harmed and how. The next step is evaluating the level of risk, whether there is a high or low chance of an individual being harmed by the hazard and whether the existing precautions in place are adequate to reduce the risk to an acceptable level, or should more be done? After the assessment, all findings should be recorded and the assessment reviewed where necessary. This may be when a new machine, substance or procedure is introduced which could lead to a new hazard or post injury or illness. For best practice review annually.

One of the best tools to assist in returning injured or ill employees to work is a well designed risk assessment (sometimes known as job analysis). Risk assessment, or job analysis, should not be confused, as is frequently done, with the human resource version of job descriptions which is often narrative in format and includes education, experience and requirements for the job. The risk assessment as described above will be a formal examination of the tasks associated with the job, including a description of the essential physical and environmental requirements of the job.

Many employers see this as a very time consuming activity, but will however discover that time invested proactively undertaking risk assessment through reviewing the job, identifying the essential job functions and documenting risk assessments formally, can be beneficial when recruiting staff into their post as well as reduce potential litigation and reduce financial cost resulting from ill health and injury.

In cases where an individual has incurred a work-related injury or illness, it is best practice to review the risk assessment, to assess whether the existing control measures are suitable and sufficient. Prior to recommending a rehabilitation programme, the OHNA, who is best placed for this role along with the health and safety advisor and line manager as they are familiar with the work hazards and environment, should undertake a risk assessment. Following assessment and taking into consideration the employee's current health status the OHNA can then make recommendations as to fitness to work and recommend the most suitable rehabilitation programme for the employee. Every effort should be made to focus on the employee's capabilities, not disabilities, when it comes to essential functions of a particular job. For example, should an employee have recently torn a ligament in their ankle that restricts them from climbing ladders or prolonged standing for the next month, but their job does not require them to climb ladders or stand for prolonged periods, then they may be able to return to their original job – perhaps with a few restrictions. However, consideration will need to be taken to travel to and from work, and in particular to access and egress into the workplace in the case of an emergency.

When recuperative duties may not be relevant   3.14

Some conditions are self-limiting and will not require recuperative duties, eg influenza, acute infections etc. Others may have an inbuilt safety net, or the GP will have recognised the demands of the job and advised sickness absence until a return to full duties is possible. For these, recuperative duties may not be necessary.

Examples of when recuperative duties are inappropriate are:

• when an employee's condition remains too serious or acute;

• for employees who are being partially treated for or newly diagnosed with a psychiatric disorder, eg schizophrenia (may cause serious disruption at the workplace);

- if the issue is a skill loss;

- for expectant or breast feeding mothers who are in good health;

- minor injuries or dental work;

- if the employee is physically unable to do much or attend regularly; or

- when the issues are predominantly caused by familial or social difficulties – in this instance special leave may be more appropriate.

Recuperative duties   3.15

There are many ways of managing sickness absence depending on the nature, type of illness and prognosis for a full recovery. In cases where an employee has been on long-term sickness absence and is expected to return to work, it may be helpful to consider a graduated and structured return to work.

Such an approach may include:

- a reduction in the hours worked each day or week;

- ergonomic adaptations to workstation or equipment used;

- workplace adaptations;

- carrying out partial duties;

- restrict repetitive movements;

- no prolonged sitting or standing;

- no excessive lifting, twisting, reaching above heights or bending;

- advice with regard to commuting or taxis;

- working on specific projects which are not too lengthy or complex;

- working from home or at a location nearer home;

- retraining; or

- temporary redeployment.

Case scenarios and suitable rehabilitative programmes   3.16

The following text provides case scenarios that are based on every day experiences of issues that confront OHNA. Guidance is provided on the management of the cases by the line manager, the OHNA and the rehabilitative programmes that could be offered.

Musculoskeletal   3.17

Case study 3

Amanda, a 24-year-old, has been working for the past three years as an operator on the assembly line of a car manufacturing company, where she daily uses a rivet gun. She attends work one day with a bandage around her right wrist and complains of being in constant pain. Her poor performance that day is noted by her manager who arranges a meeting with Amanda to discuss this.

Line manager responsibilities

- Discuss health concerns and performance with Amanda.

- Arrange referral to occupational health for early assessment and intervention.

- Provide Amanda with alternative temporary work until advice sought by occupational health as to fitness to undertake full duties.

Occupational health nurse advisor responsibilities

On receipt of referral, the OHNA should undertake the following.

- Health assessment – physical, psychological and social.

- Identify causative factors – work or non-work related issue.

- Explore history – past or present.

- Attain information regarding investigations or treatment to date.

- If no intervention to date – arrange referral to GP or occupational health physician for diagnosis.

- Referral to physiotherapy for assessment and treatment.

- Provide with appropriate health advice for effective self-management.

- Referral to health and safety adviser, physiotherapist or OHNA to undertake ergonomic risk assessment of workstation and task undertaken.

- Develop an agreed rehabilitation plan, eg recuperative duties.

  - Initially while symptomatic, give advice refraining from using the rivet gun and offer alternative duties that do not incorporate use of same muscle groups.

  - As symptoms resolve or when asymptomatic, encourage gradual re-introduction to activity on a daily or weekly basis depending on health needs. Gradually increase time over a six to eight-week

period. Time scales will vary with each client and will be dependant on the health review assessment.

o   Discourage prolonged repetitive movements and hence introduce
job rotation every two to three hours within the organisation, so
that different muscle groups are used and provide time for muscles
to rest and recover. Each task included in a rotation programme
should be qualitatively different from the preceding and succeed-
ing operation.

o   Encourage rest breaks to operator. Short frequent breaks are more
effective than longer, irregular breaks.

o   Ergonomic adaptations post risk assessment may be required to a
workbench in order to raise or lower it, or modification to a rivet
gun to enable comfort and to ensure accurate ergonomic posture
is adopted when handling.

Case study 4

Colin works as a production operator in a printing factory. The department
has been short staffed for over a week and has resulted in overtime work for
Colin. What would normally have been assessed as a two-man lift, Colin in
order to save time, has been lifting on his own (a job that he has done easily
for the past 20 years unaided before implementation of any health and safety
recommendations of 25kg maximum weight to be lifted). Before going home
he does the final lift of the day but looses grip of the bulk, twists awkwardly
and falls to the floor. He has noticeably sustained a back injury. He visits his
GP who certificates him off work for two weeks with acute back injury.

Line manager responsibilities

●   Arrange immediate health assessment by occupational health, GP or
local hospital depending on severity and accessibility of services at time
of injury.

●   Complete accident form – commence accident investigation by attain-
ing all relevant facts.

●   Arrange referral to occupational health for early assessment and onward
referral for physiotherapy services if appropriate.

●   Keep in regular contact with Colin while off work.

●   Review risk assessment and assess whether control measures in place are
suitable and sufficient, or whether more needs to be put in place.

(cont'd)

- On return to work and following completion of accident investigation, dependant on findings, commence disciplinary procedure for misconduct or poor performance and failure to comply with health and safety procedures if applicable.

- Retraining in safe manual handling operations.

- Supervision.

- Agree rehabilitation plan and monitor progress until fit for full duties.

Occupational health nurse advisor responsibilities

On receipt of referral, the OHNA should undertake the following.

- Health assessment – physical, psychological and/or social.

- Identify causative factors – work or non-work related issue.

- Explore history – past or present.

- Attain information regarding investigations or treatment to date.

- If no intervention to date – arrange physiotherapy referral for assessment and treatment.

- Provide Colin with appropriate health advice on care of back and safe handling of loads.

- Review manual handling risk assessment with line manager or health and safety manager, and modify if required.

- Develop an agreed rehabilitation plan. This may incorporate recuperative duties of:

  o initially while symptomatic, advice refraining from:

  – heavy manual handling activity,

  – no prolonged sitting or standing,

  – no excessive bending,

  – no twisting and excessive reaching,

  o reduced hours of work initially, gradually increasing by an hour each week over a six to eight-week period; and

  o as symptoms resolve or when asymptomatic encourage gradual reintroduction to manual handling activity post risk assessment.

Job design and work organisational factors   **3.18**

There are many considerations to be applied to workstations, workplaces and equipment to enable employees to work comfortably, safely and contently.

Job and work organisation factors, such as speed of operation, rest breaks and rotation programmes also need to be carefully designed as they will determine how individuals relate to each other and with the production systems in existence.

The following factors should be considered in job design, to be beneficial to both worker and the organisation.

- **Motivation**. An individual's effectiveness will no doubt be influenced by their motivation, in a motivated state the individual will be more likely to perform as they will identify their work as been challenging and meaningful and where their contribution is recognised within the organisation.

- **Managing organisational change**. Any changes to take place should be managed and introduced with care. Where possible involve the workforce as much as possible as this will influence the level of acceptance among the workforce. Any changes should be evaluated to ensure that they have become part of a well-adjusted work system.

- **Repetition**. Repetitive tasks should be avoided and where they exist job rotation should be used to reduce the risk of injury, boredom and monotony. Multi-skilling or job enlargement is best adopted, so that the employee in multi-skilling is trained to complete any operation within a given area and through job enlargement, increases the number of tasks to be undertaken which reduces the effect of repetitive tasks. Both offer greater variety. Job enrichment is another factor worth considering, giving the operator more responsibility for their own work and a greater contribution in the decision making process.

- **Work rate**. Operators should be encouraged to work at a consistent work rate throughout the day and from day-to-day. Where possible, peaks and troughs in activity should be avoided, since increasing the workload, whereby the worker has to work faster, also increases their fatigue and the likelihood of sustaining a strain or injury.

- **Workload**. Operators should where possible be given an opportunity to become accustomed to the demands of any new or recently altered task before they are expected to produce a set level of output. This will facilitate them to develop a level of work hardening or task fitness which will reduce the risk of injury.

- **Rest breaks**. Rest breaks should be made available at regular intervals. Micro pauses, lasting only a few seconds should be designed into tasks if possible, as this will provide a brief respite from the stresses of the overall task. For example a display screen user would stop to read their screen at regular intervals.

57

- **Financial incentives – bonus from overtime**. Bonuses of payment are not always ideal since they encourage the operator to work faster, for longer periods of time and with few if any rest breaks. Additionally, the increase in the individual's exposure to their working environment and it's associated hazards, in particular if the task involves repetition, deviation of the wrists, force, static movement or cold temperatures to mention only a few. Hence any overtime work should not only be viewed as a benefit for the organisation and individual, but viewed also in terms of its disadvantages.

- **Work schedules/shift work**. The type of work schedule adopted, whether it be continental twelve-hour shifts or a three eight-hour shift system incorporating night work will influence attendance, motivation and commitment. Consideration should be given to commitments outside work, with more family friendly work schedules being adopted. Additionally, due to the changes in circadian rhythms, it will take two weeks for a night worker to become adjusted to the unnatural day sleep, night work pattern. The type of rotation applied should be carefully considered.

- **Automation**. The effects of automation on the workforce should be considered since this can lead to changes in the level of control and responsibility combined with the changed demands and interaction between other workers.

Mental health   3.19

Case study 5

Mr Pickard has been promoted to supervisor within the finance department. No formal training has been given for this role. Several members of staff are off sick within the department and no cover has been arranged. Over the past six weeks the manager has noted a pattern of frequent short-term sickness absence by Mr Pickard, a general apathy towards his work and persistent lateness. His manager arranges a meeting to discuss these issues. Mr Pickard calls in sick the morning of his interview and a week later is signed off by his GP for a month with depression.

Line manager responsibilities

- Keep in regular contact with Mr Pickard while he is absent from work, remaining supportive.

- Discuss reason for absence with Mr Pickard and advise Mr Pickard of the support services available from occupational health and notify him of referral.

- Arrange referral to occupational health for early assessment and intervention.

- Post occupational health assessment and management advice provided, should one agree, then co-operate to the agreed rehabilitation programme.

- Undertake work-stress risk assessment or job analysis and modify where required.

- Undertake detailed return to work interview.

- Provide Mr Pickard with ongoing support and supervision.

- Provide training, if identified.

Occupational health nurse advisor responsibilities

On receipt of referral, the OHNA should undertake the following.

- Health assessment – physical, psychological, social, and work-life balance.

- Explore psychological issues in terms of work and non-work related issue.

- Explore history – past, present medical history and family history.

- Attain information regarding investigations or treatment to date.

- If no intervention to date – liaise with GP for diagnosis and treatment (medication if appropriate).

- Referral to employee advisory service for counselling, in particular cognitive behavioural therapy.

- Referral to specialist for assessment if appropriate, eg psychiatrist.

- Liaise with line manager to undertake a work-stress risk assessment and modify the job where stressors are identified.

- Liaise with manager to arrange training or supervision.

- Arrange rehabilitation programme. This may include:

  o graded return to work, reduced hours initially gradually increasing each week over a six to eight-week period;

  o working on specific projects which are not too lengthy or complex;

  o as symptoms resolve or when asymptomatic, encourage gradual re-introduction to normal duties;

  o ongoing support through regular occupational health review; and

  o case conferences with all disciplines to discuss progress in matters that are sensitive or complex, to assist resolve situation.

- Provide with appropriate health advice on work-life balance and healthy lifestyle.

- Encourage line manager to undertake a stress management course, so to identify stress in others and gain basic stress management techniques within the workplace.

Case study 6

Dennis is a 45-year-old employee who has suffered a recent bereavement of a family member under very traumatic circumstances. He is understandably very traumatised by the situation and is having difficulty coming to terms with it all. Dennis feels that the only 'stable' thing in his life at the moment is his work and is adamant that he would like to continue working as usual. However, he is often upset whilst sitting at his desk and his manager and colleagues are very concerned. Dennis has been working for the company for 17 years and is employed as reception administrator.

Line manager responsibilities

- Discuss health concerns and performance issues with Dennis.
- Arrange referral to occupational health for early assessment and intervention.
- Provide Dennis with alternative temporary work away from reception area until advice sought by occupational health as to fitness to undertake full duties.
- Thereafter, post assessment and management advice, assuming there is agreement, then there needs to be co-operation to adhere to the agreed rehabilitation programme.
- Provide Dennis with ongoing support and supervision.
- Carry out job analysis where workload is assessed in particular and modify as required.

Occupational health nurse advisor responsibilities

On receipt of referral, the OHNA should undertake the following.

- Health assessment – physical, psychological, social and work–life balance.
- Explore psychological issues in terms of work, non-work related issue.
- Explore history – past, present medical history and family history.
- Attain information regarding investigations or treatment to date.
- If no intervention to date – liaise with GP or occupational health physician for diagnosis and treatment (medication if appropriate).
- Referral to employee advisory service for counselling or therapy such as cognitive behavioural therapy which can be beneficial.
- Referral to specialist for assessment if appropriate, eg psychiatrist.

- Liaise with line manager to undertake a work-stress risk assessment.

- Advice from rehabilitation programme – this may include:

  o graded return to work in that of initial reduced hours if appropriate;

  o counselling therapy in that of cognitive behavioural therapy;

  o temporary relocation away from the busy reception area to an area less public, but remaining to work with his fellow colleagues for support;

  o work adjustments in that of volume of workload and level of responsibility; and

  o ongoing occupational health support through regular reviews.

Best practice in mental health rehabilitation   3.20

- Early contact between employee and employer. The organisation will need to consider who is best placed to have initial contact with the employee, avoiding further distress, particularly if known work-related problem.

- Timing of health assessment – early referral to occupational health within a two to four-week time period is advocated for early diagnosis, treatment and ongoing rehabilitation.

- Developing and agreed rehabilitation plan – rehabilitation plan should be developed with agreed realistic time frames when appropriate and agreed by all parties. Commitment should be assured by all parties and programme reviewed at regular intervals formally.

- Availability of therapeutic interventions – referral to occupational health should be instigated so that assessment of health needs can be made and onward referral to appropriate health professionals for treatment or therapeutic interventions, eg counselling can proceed.

- Flexible return to work options – a graded return to work is well recognised as beneficial and may include adjustment to hours, the job or the work location.

- Work adaptations and adjustments – it is beneficial that a work-stress risk assessment is undertaken and where harmful work aspects are recognised, that these be changed or removed, enabling the employee to return to the job which will not aggravate their illness or impede their recovery.

Not all rehabilitation programmes implemented will be successful; some of the obstacles to effective rehabilitation can be as follows.

(cont'd)

- Process barriers.

  o Diagnosis, eg misdiagnosis of a problem, delayed diagnosis or the failure of management or employee to accept the problem and deal with it.

  o Timing, eg delayed referral to occupational health for management advice, assessment and treatment of the employee.

  o Communication or consistency of approach, eg unclear guidelines on the rehabilitation programme agreed and the inconsistent approach and commitment to rehabilitation programmes within the organisation.

  o Resources. This may involve lack of resources in that of staffing to provide adequate cover, time, funds as well as accessibility to treatment.

- Cultural barriers.

  o Trust. A lack of mutual trust or scepticism by the employee can cause a threat to successful rehabilitation, therefore effective communication is required by all parties, respect for the individual, confidentiality and a sensitive approach taken when dealing with the employee.

  o Managers. A lack of commitment and understanding to mental health issues and importance of a graded return to work by the manager can result in an unsuccessful rehabilitation. Many managers, due to operational feasibility and lack of understanding, prefer the employee to return to work on full duties since this is operationally easier.

  o Employees. Poor compliance or lack of commitment by the employee can be a threat to effective rehabilitation. Additionally, when there is a claim being made by the employee or pending litigation this can detract from an effective rehabilitation as the employee and the organisation are likely to be at odds.

  o Staff. Sometimes resentment can develop by other colleagues towards an employee who is working reduced hours or modified duties, due to lack of understanding of the employee's personal circumstances.

- Health care disciplines involved in rehabilitation.

Counselling and EAPs   **3.21**

The demands of today's work and home life may leave many an employee unable to cope, feeling disempowered and seeking help and support. One source of help may be counselling. Counsellors can help an employee during periods of distress, crisis and/or change to arrive at their own decisions and choices.

Proactive stress management interventions services are widely accepted as beneficial in health care intervention to reduce mental health related sickness absence. Although there is limited empirical evidence of reduced health care cost in effective treatment of mental health issues such as depression or anxiety, there is growing evidence of productivity improvements resulting from early intervention, and these may in themselves offset the cost of the treatment to an organisation. Counsellors, along with occupational health nurse advisors, can implement appropriate programmes to meet organisational and individual needs.

A proactive organisational approach to work-related stress through training, communication and supervision, together with risk assessment is advocated. It is also recommended that identification of hazards to health, and implementation of individual or organisational initiatives to control exposure through health promotion and management policies is effective in reducing mental health issues and consequently cost from sickness absence within an organisation. Promoting best practice to a larger audience will no doubt be more beneficial and cheaper than reactionary cognitive behavioural therapy on an individual basis.

Physiotherapy services   **3.22**

Back pain and other musculoskeletal problems are being identified as the biggest health concerns and the greatest cause of absence to organisations. Whether they are work-related or not, musculoskeletal problems, such as bone, muscular or joint problems can be very disabling for an individual and lead to extensive time off work in some cases. Additionally, in some cases, particularly if work related, this can lead to employee litigation as well as increased insurance costs for the employer.

To provide physiotherapy services within an organisation is a valuable service, particularly if on-site, since it provides employees with much faster access to treatment through an early referral by occupational health. Easy access to such services will most often lead to quicker rehabilitation, less likelihood of recurrences, less time off work and a reduction in employee ill health retirements.

Physiotherapists, as part of a multi-disciplinary team, can work with occupational heath and safety practitioners by identifying workplace ergonomic problems, such as those encountered from working with display screen equipment or those employees who carry out manual handling activities. Problems can be identified, that can then result in changes in duties or modifications made to equipment or workstations.

A physiotherapist working alongside the occupational health team can monitor an employee's progress in treatment and adapt any rehabilitative intervention accordingly.

Fitness centres and the role of fitness instructors 3.23

Qualified and experienced fitness instructors based either within the physiotherapy department or located with the organisation's gymnasium can work collaboratively with physiotherapists in employee rehabilitation, particularly in cases of backcare management. Once the employee has made a steady recovery from a back problem the fitness instructor can further support the employee by providing strengthening exercises, increase flexibility and improve general fitness of the individual, hopefully reducing recurrence.

Internal and external provision of occupational health services 3.24

Occupational health services will differ in their provision from in-house to an external provider, their destination, whether on or off-site, as well as service provision. All of these decisions are primarily influenced by the organisation's business needs, financial circumstances, identified risks, the degree to which the contribution of the employee's health to the business is recognised and its regard to occupational health service in assisting them on issues of workers health and fitness to work.

Models of services available vary from:

- individual model of practice; and
- group model of practice.

Individual model of practice 3.25

This model focuses on single health issues. It is based on the traditional medical model of practice that has been revised and adopted by occupational health services. If an employee becomes ill or injured, they would routinely visit the occupational health department for treatment should it be a physical ailment, or for counselling if the issue was psychological in nature. The treatment would usually consist of direct, hands-on care such as measuring blood pressure, changing a dressing, giving inoculations or issuing medication, such as analgesia if the employee complained of pain. Treatment would be provided be it occupational or non-occupational in origin. Additionally, in many organisations sought after the facilities of nurses and physicians for health surveillance screening, such as carrying out hearing tests, lung functions tests and skin inspection, will depend on the hazards and risk identified.

Group model of practice 3.26

This approach is a more holistic approach to health care, promoting the highest level of physical, psychological and social wellbeing for all individuals. The number of services to be made available will be defined by the business needs, hazards and risks assessed and importantly the finance available to source. Facilities that can be available within the model will include:

- occupational health – incorporating:
  - ○ pre-employment screening,
  - ○ health surveillance,
  - ○ health promotion or education,
  - ○ policy development,
  - ○ travel health,
  - ○ case management (sickness absence management),
  - ○ first aid,
- physiotherapy services;
- dental service;
- chiropody services; and
- counselling services.

There are many ways of providing occupational health services, these can range from:

- in-house sole provider;
- contract service – sole supplier; and
- contract service – multi supplier.

To each of the above type of service provision there are many advantages and disadvantages. When an organisation decides on the type of service delivery, such as an in-house service, particular consideration should be made to the following factors:

- advantages to in-house service:
  - ○ part of the business,
  - ○ knowledge of the organisation's function, culture and needs,
  - ○ commitment to the organisation,
  - ○ known and trusted by the organisation,
- disadvantages to an in-house service can be:

○   limited experience,

○   finite resource,

○   financial issues,

○   credibility.

For these reasons an employer may choose external services, where the entire contract is supplied by a sole provider or where a contract of services is chosen and supplied by multiple suppliers:

● advantages to external services:

○   clear agreement,

○   direct support,

○   flexibility,

○   emergency cover,

● disadvantages to external service provision can be:

○   occupational health practitioner not 'engaged',

○   turnover of staff,

○   no follow through.

Each organisation should weigh up the advantages and disadvantages of each type of service for their organisation and decide on what meets their needs and fits in to their organisation's culture:

● in summary, service available from occupational health can range from:

○   treatment or practice,

○   advisory,

○   single site or multi-site,

○   travelling – where the occupational health practitioner travels from on site to another within the same organisation.

Benefits of a multi-disciplinary approach in health care   3.27

The complexity of the workplace today demands that occupational health does not work in isolation, and that organisations view the delivery of occupational health as a collaborative initiative between management, health care professionals, employees and health and safety practitioners.

Occupational health is a support service that can, when used effectively, assist an organisation move towards a more productive partnership between employers and employees. It is purely an advisory service for both management and employee, and is not enforcing in any way.

It is now know that the main ill health contributors to absence from work are likely to be musculoskeletal, stress or cardiovascular in nature. To tackle these within the workplace specialist health professionals, such as ergonomists, physio-therapist, occupational psychologist and counsellors, along with occupational health nurse advisors and physicians are required who have specialist knowledge of health implications in the workplace. The benefits of accessibility to all these services through an integrated occupational health service, working along side primarily health care facilities, will undoubtedly contribute to better rehabilitation of the employee and an earlier return to work.

Chapter 4
Legal Compliance

The Law, Occupational Health and Rehabilitation   4.1

The *Health and Safety at Work etc. Act 1974 (HSWA 1974)* is the cornerstone of health and safety law in the UK. Employers have a wide ranging duty to protect the health, safety and welfare of employees. Specific duties, eg risk assessment and health surveillance, are contained in regulations made under *HSWA 1974* and other legislation such as the *Management of Health and Safety at Work Regulations (MHSWR) 1999 (SI 1999 No 3242)*. However, unlike certain other European Union member states, there is no legislation which specifically place a duty upon employers to provide occupation health services.

The *Disability Discrimination Act 1995 (DDA 1995)* requires employers to treat disabled people equally with non-disabled people in all employment matters and make reasonable adjustments that may be necessary to enable the disabled employee to be able to work. Occupational health support can be important in assisting employers to act in a way that does not discriminate against disabled employees contrary to *DDA 1995*.

There is no legal duty upon employers to provide rehabilitation for people who become disabled while in employment, even for workers injured or made ill in the course of their work.

Both the Association of British Insurers (ABI) and the Trades Union Congress (TUC) recognise that it is important to get people back to work as soon as possible if they have been injured. They have worked together promoting rehabilitation with the message of rehabilitation being good for the employee and good for business.

However rehabilitation all too often only gets considered when there is a claim for compensation by the injured employee. By the time rehabilitation is offered it is either too late, or it has little chance of being as effective as it would have been if it had been offered soon after the employee was injured.

In April 2003 the Government started a two-year pilot scheme, funded by the Department for Works and Pensions (DWP), in relation to rehabilitation. The purpose of the scheme is to determine how best to use rehabilitation. That is to say whether it is best to concentrate on medical treatment for the injury the person has sustained, to modify the working environment to cope with the injury or whether a mixture of the two is required. The scheme will help to advise ministers about future Government policy with the possible roll-out of a new national service for rehabilitation.

In April 2004 the DWP issued a document entitled: *Developing a framework for vocational rehabilitation: a discussion paper* which introduced plans for a framework for rehabilitation (available at: www.dwp.gov.uk/consultations/2004/index.asp). This sets out a framework for rehabilitation to help people overcome health or disability-related barriers to a successful return to work

In June 2000 the Government and the Health and Safety Commission (HSC) launched its strategy statement *Revitalising Health and Safety*. Within this strategy there were certain aspirations in respect of occupational health and rehabilitation. (Health and Safety Commission, *Revitalising health and safety strategy statement*, Department of Environment, Transport and the Regions, Wetherby, 2000.)

The first action point was for the HSC to work with a range of Government departments and other partners to promote and implement fully a new occupational health strategy for the UK. This was commenced in July 2000 and work is still undergoing.

A second action point was that the Government would encourage better access to occupational health support, and promote occupational health in local Health Improvement Programmes and Primary Care Group strategies. Work still continues in this respect.

Another action point was that as part of the New Deal for Disabled People, the Government would consider how best to strengthen retention and rehabilitation services for people in work who became disabled or who have persistent sickness. The HSE is developing a best practice guide for employers on managing sickness and recovery of health at work to help them support the return to work and continued employment of ill and injured workers. The HSE is also developing a tool for employers to help them collect, record and measure sickness absence so that they can target areas where ill health and injury might be a problem. The HSE aims to publish the guide and tool by the end of 2004.

The next action point was for the HSC to consult on whether the duty upon employers under health and safety law to ensure the continuing health of employees at work, including action to rehabilitate where appropriate, can usefully be clarified or strengthened. The HSC has taken the view that a primary legislative vehicle may become available. In the meantime the HSE should continue with the DWP and Department of Health to take forward the job retention and rehabilitation agenda.

The final action point was to ensure that health and safety is never used as a false excuse for not employing, or continuing to employ a disabled person. The HSC has now published research on this issue. The HSC and the Disability Rights Commission is now in discussions as to how best to address these concerns. ('The extent of use of health and safety requirements as a false excuse for not employing sick or disabled persons', *Health and Safety Commission*, HSE Research Report No 167, HSE Books, 2003 (download at www.hse.gov.uk).)

In May 2004 the Better Regulation Task Force published its report *Better Routes to Redress*. (This can be downloaded at www.brtf.gov.uk/taskforce/reports/8874betterroutes.pdf.) This said there is a commonly held perception, fuelled by the media, that the UK is in the grip of a 'compensation culture'. The report says this is an 'urban myth'. However it goes on to say that this perception causes the real problem: the fear of litigation impacts on behaviour and imposes burdens on organisations trying to handle claims. The report makes a number of recommendations some of which relate to rehabilitation and occupational health.

In relation to rehabilitation the Task Force has recommended:

• the Chief Medical Officer should lead a cross-Department group to assess the economic benefits of greater National Health Service (NHS)-provided rehabilitation; and

• the DWP should lead a group, which includes insurers, lawyers, HSE, the NHS and other interested parties, to look at developing mechanisms for earlier access to rehabilitation.

It is envisaged that both groups should make recommendations by February 2005.

In relation to occupational health, the Task Force recommends that the HSE should publicise better information on the beneficial tax provisions relating to employers purchasing occupational health support.

Thus whilst there is promotion and encouragement for occupational health and rehabilitation, there is in fact no legal requirement to have these. Having said this the prudent employer is advised to have available occupation health services and a policy on the use of rehabilitation.

Health and Safety Regulation 4.2

This section considers the general health and safety law applicable in the UK.

Health and Safety at Work etc. Act 1974 (HSWA 1974) 4.3

The essential purpose of *Health and Safety at Work etc. Act 1974* (*HSWA 1974*) is to secure the health, safety and welfare of employees at work and to protect non-employees from the activities of a company's business (see *HSWA 1974, s 1*). *HSWA 1974* sets out a number of general duties upon employers (and also their employees).

The main duties upon employers are set out in *HSWA 1974, ss 2–3*.

HSWA 1974, s 2(1) states:

71

'It shall be the duty of every employer to ensure so far as is reasonably practicable, the health and safety and welfare at work of all its employees'.

HSWA 1974, s 2(2)(c) requires employers provide its employees with 'such information, instruction, training and supervision as is necessary to ensure, so far as is reasonably practicable, the health and safety at work' of its employees. *HSWA 1974, s 2(2)(e)* also requires employers to provide and maintain a working environment of its employees that is 'so far as is reasonably practicable, safe without risks to health, and adequate as regards facilities and arrangements for their welfare at work'.

HSWA 1974, s 2(3) additionally requires employers, who employ more than five people, to prepare and, as often as necessary revise, a health and safety statement and to bring the statement and any revision to the notice of employees.

HSWA 1974, s 3(1) states:

'It shall be the duty of every employer to conduct his undertaking in such a way as to ensure, so far as is reasonably practicable, that persons not in his employment who may be effected thereby are not thereby exposed to risks to their health and safety'.

Section 3(1) would apply to self-employed persons working at an employer's business. It should be noted that for them, whilst this section refers to their 'health and safety' it does not refer to their welfare.

Reasonably practicable 4.4

The important words in the sections of the *Health and Safety at Work etc. Act 1974* given above are: '*so far as is reasonably practicable*'. The test as to what is reasonably practicable was set out in the case of *Edwards v National Coal Board [1949] 1 AER 743*. This case established the risk must be balanced against the 'sacrifice', whether in money, time or trouble, needed to avert or mitigate the risk. By carrying out this exercise the employer can determine what measures are reasonable to take. This is effectively an implied requirement for a risk assessment.

Enforcement of Health and Safety at Work etc. Act 1974 (HSWA 1974) 4.5

A breach of one of the duties under the *Health and Safety at Work etc. Act 1974 (HSWA 1974)* cannot give rise to a civil claim for compensation if someone is injured as a result of the breach. However a breach of the *HSWA* can amount to a criminal offence (even if no one is injured as a consequence).

The HSC issued its latest enforcement policy statement in January 2002 that outlines when and how the HSE and other health and safety enforcing authorities (eg local authorities) will take action to investigate and prosecute companies for breaches of health and safety law. 'Enforcement policy statement' (HSC15), Health and Safety Commission, HSE Books, 2002 (available from HSE Books, PO Box 1999, Sudbury, Suffolk, CO10 2WA, tel: 01787 881165, fax: 01787 313995, website: www.hsebooks.co.uk).) The statement can also be viewed on its website at: www.hse.gov.uk/pubns/hsc15.pdf.

Prosecutions under *HSWA 1974* in certain circumstances follow on from the service of an improvement notice of a prohibition notice upon the company.

If a health and safety inspector believes safety legislation is being breached, he or she can issue an improvement notice requiring action to be taken by the company concerned in order to improve safety. The notice specifies which legislation is being breached and gives the company a period of time (usually at least 21 days) to correct the defect or hazardous situation.

If however the inspector believes that a work activity poses a serious risk of personal injury, he or she can issue a prohibition notice. This stops the activity. Unlike an improvement notice, an inspector does not have to believe there has been a breach of health and safety law to issue the prohibition notice, which is served in anticipation of danger. Further, if the inspector believes the risk of injury is imminent, the notice can take immediate effect.

In 2003 West Dorset General Hospitals NHS Trust became the first ever employer to be served with an enforcement notice in respect of stress by HSE. It was served following a complaint by a member of staff to the HSE which resulted in an inspector carrying out an investigation. The inspector discussed with the Trust measures needed to tackle the problem and also discussed and agreed a deadline for compliance.

Management of Health and Safety at Work Regulations (MHSWR) 1999 (SI 1999 No 3242) 4.6

Breach of the *Management of Health and Safety at Work Regulations (MHSWR) 1999 (SI 1999 No 3242)*, like the duties under the *Health and Safety at Work etc. Act 1974 (HSWA 1974)*, can amount to a criminal offence (that may be prosecuted by the HSE). Originally a breach did not give rise to a civil action. However *SI 1999 No 3242* and the *Fire Precautions (Workplace) (Amendment) Regulations 1997 (SI 1997 No 1840)* (which came into force on 27 October 2003) modify this exclusion. These now allow employees (but not non-employees) to bring a civil action for a breach of *SI 1999 No 3242*.

The obligation upon employers to carry out 'general' risk assessments is contained in *SI 1999 No 3242, Reg 3* (these regulations supersede the 1992 Regulations of the same name), which states:

'(1)   Every employer shall make a suitable and sufficient assessment of:

(a)   the risks to the health and safety of his employees to which they are exposed whilst they are at work; and

(b)   the risks to the health and safety of persons not in his employment arising out of or in connection with the conduct by him of his undertaking

for the purpose of identifying the measures he needs to take to comply with the requirement and prohibitions imposed upon him, by or under the relevant statutory provision and by Part II of the Fire Precautions (Workplace) Regulations 1997.'

Therefore if there is a hazard, it needs to be assessed and the appropriate control measures need to be put in place in order to reduce the risk to an acceptable level.

Hierarchy of control measures

The priority to be given to the application of types of control measures is set out in *SI 1999 No 3242, Sch 1* of the Regulations. The hierarchy of control measures are as follows:

(a)   avoid risks;

(b)   evaluating the risks which cannot be avoided;

(c)   combat the risks at source;

(d)   adapt the work to the individual, especially as regards the design of workplaces, the choice of work, equipment and the choice of working and production method, with a view in particular to alleviating monotonous work and work at predetermined work rate and to reducing their effect on health;

(e)   adapt to technical process;

(f)   replace the dangerous by the non-dangerous or the less dangerous;

(g)   develop a coherent overall prevention policy that covers technology, organisation of work, working conditions, social relationships and the influence of factors relating to the working environment;

(h)   give collective protective measures priority over individual protective measures; and

(i)   give appropriate instructions to employees.

It was held by the Court of Appeal in *R v Board of Trustees of the Science Museum [1993] 1 WLR 1171* that the term 'risk' denotes the *possibility* of danger rather than *actual* danger.

Paragraph 11 of the Approved Code of Practice (ACOP), to *SI 1999 No 3242*, which sets out the requirement for risk assessments, gives a definition of risk. It states that risk is the *likelihood* of potential harm from a hazard being *realised*. A 'hazard' is defined as something with the potential to cause harm. The extent of the risk, according to the ACOP, depends on: (i) the likelihood of that harm occurring; (ii) the potential severity of that harm, and (iii) the population which might be affected by that harm. (*Management of Health and Safety at Work Regulations 1999*, Approved Code of Practice & Guidance, L21, ISBN 0 7178 2488 9, available from HSE Books.)

In *Koonjul v Thameslink Healthcare Services [2000] PIQR P123*, the Court of Appeal considered the issue of risk for the purposes of *Regulation 4* of the *Manual Handling Operations Regulations 1992 (SI 1991 No 2793)*, which requires a specific risk assessment to be carried out by employers in relation to manual handling operations performed by employees. Lady Justice Hale (at p126) in considering the level of risk which is required to bring a case within *Regulation 4*, said:

> '…there must be a real risk, a foreseeable possibility of injury; certainly nothing approaching a probability.'

The importance of risk assessments was stressed in the Court of Appeal case of *Griffiths v Vauxhall Motors [2003] EWCA Civ 412* in which Lord Justice Clarke said:

> 'The whole point of a proper risk assessment is that an investigation is carried out in order to identify whether the particular operation gives rise to any risk to safety and, if so, what is the extent of that risk, which of course includes the extent of any risk of injury, and what can and should be done to minimise or eradicate the risk.'

Risk assessment and risk management are distinct. Risk management addresses the *appraisal* of assessed risk and the *making of decisions* concerning risks, in particular safety measures and their subsequent implementation. The carrying out of risk assessment does not remove from managers the responsibility for safety decisions, but forms an important part of making decisions about health and safety.

SI 1991 No 2793, Reg 5 states:

> 'Every employer shall make and give effect to such arrangements as are appropriate, having regard to the nature of his activities and the size of his undertaking, for the effective planning, organisation, control, monitoring and review of the preventative and proactive measures.'

Risk management is a continual process, which includes the following.

- **Policy:** aims and objectives to be achieved, informed by risk profile or other risk assessment outputs and defining measures for success of failure.
- **Planning:** the steps to be taken to manage the identified risks.
- **Implementation:** rolling out and executing the plan.
- **Monitoring:** checking on progress against objectives through audit, performance measurements, incident or accident investigation and management review.

This approach is amplified in the HSE's guide *Successful health and safety management* (HSG65) and applies risk assessment as a basis for good management by ordinary good practice. (Health and Safety Executive, *Successful health and safety management*, ISBN 0 7176 1276 7, HS(G)65, second edition, HSE Books, Sudbury, 1997.)

SI 1999 No 3242, Reg 6 of the *MHSWR* concerns health surveillance and states:

> 'Every employer shall ensure that his employees are provided with such health surveillance as is appropriate having regard to the risks to their health and safety which are identified by the assessment.'

Paragraph 41 of the ACOP of the Regulations says the risk assessment will identify circumstances in which health surveillance is require by specific health and safety regulations, eg *Control of Substances Hazardous to Health Regulations (COSHH) 2002*. (*Management of Health and Safety at Work Regulations 1999*, Approved Code of Practice & Guidance, L21, ISBN 0 7178 2488 9, available from HSE Books.) It advises that health surveillance should also be introduced where the following criteria apply:

(a) there is an identifiable disease or adverse health condition related to the work concerned;

(b) valid techniques are available to detect indications of the disease or condition;

(c) there is a reasonable likelihood that the disease or condition may occur under the particular conditions of work; and

(d) surveillance is likely to further the protection of the health and safety of the employees to be covered.

Paragraph 43 of the ACOP says the appropriate level, frequency and procedure of health surveillance should be determined by a competent person 'acting within the limits of their training and experience', but in certain circumstances this may require the assistance of a medical practitioner. It goes onto say that the minimum requirement for health surveillance is keeping a health record which should be maintained throughout an employee's employment (unless the risks are rare and short term).

At paragraph 44 gives examples of health surveillance procedures which are:

(a) inspection of readily detectable conditions by a responsible person with appropriate training and experience;

(b) enquiries about symptoms, inspection and examination by a qualified person (eg an Occupational Health Nurse);

(c) medical surveillance;

(d) biological effect monitoring; and

(e) biological monitoring.

SI 1999 No 3242, Reg 7 imposes the duty upon the employer to have someone within his own organisation carry out the necessary risk assessments. This person must have the appropriate expertise and training and be provided with the appropriate information. For many companies advice from outside consultants will be the exception rather than the rule.

Under *SI 1999 No 3242, Reg 10* employers 'shall' give to employees 'comprehensible and relevant' information on risks to the employee's health and safety identified by any risk assessment and the preventative and protective measures in place.

SI 1999 No 3242, Reg 13 deals with capabilities and training of employees. It says employers 'shall' take into account an employee's capabilities in relation to the work he or she is asked to do. This is amplified in paragraph 80 of the ASCOP which states:

'When allocating work to employees, employers should ensure that the demands of the job do not exceed the employees' ability to carry out the work without risk to themselves or others…. Employers should review their employees' capabilities to carry out their work, as necessary.'

In other words when carrying out risk assessments, these can apply not only to the work but also to the employee in relation to whether he or she is able to do the work without risk to his or her and others health and safety. Thus, for example, if an employee has a particular disability, it may be a necessary factor to be risk assessed in relation to a certain type of work.

Regulation 13 also requires employers to give health and safety training when the employee starts employment with the employer and (if he or she is exposed to new or increased risks):

• when the employee is transferred to another job or his or her responsibilities change;

• new work equipment is either introduced or old work equipment is changed;

• new technology is introduced; and

• new system of work is introduced or the old system is changed.

Training has to be in working hours, adapted if there are new or changed risks and repeated periodically as appropriate.

Reporting of Injuries, Diseases and Dangerous Occurrences Regulations (RIDDOR) 1995 (SI 1995 No 3163) 4.7

These regulations requires employers to notify the HSE immediately when any person dies, suffers a serious injury, suffers an injury which requires him or her to be taken to hospital as a result of an accident at work or if there is a dangerous occurrence. A report, in prescribed form, must then be sent within ten days.

There are also provisions for the reporting of persons suffering from any of the occupational conditions specified in the Regulations and their work involves specified activities.

The reporting under the *Reporting of Injuries, Diseases and Dangerous Occurrences Regulations 1995* does not override medical confidentiality (see **4.24** below). An employer only has to report an occupational condition when a report in writing from a registered medical practitioner has been received and will need the informed consent of the employee to make a named report. An occupation health department of an employer can inform management of an increased incidence of an occupational disease providing the employees are not named.

It is an offence not to comply with *RIDDOR*. There will be a defence however if it can be shown that the reportable matter was not known of and that there were reasonable processes in place to inform the employer of such occurrences.

Stress, Back Injuries, RSI and COSHH 4.8

The law in relation to these areas are relevant to occupational health and issues relating to rehabilitation. Much of what is detailed below deals with employers' duties that have been decided in claims for compensation brought by injured employees against their employers.

Stress 4.9

The leading case upon stress is *Hatton v Sutherland and three other appeals [2002] PIQR P21*.

In each case the claimants, Hatton, Barber, Bishop and Jones were awarded compensation by a County Court. The respective defendants appealed the decisions. The main thrust of the appeals was that the courts had set the trigger for when an employer has to act too low.

The appeals of Hatton, Barber and Bishop were upheld while that of Jones was dismissed 'not without some hesitation' by the Court (but see below Barber's appeal to the House of Lords). Hatton and Barber were teachers in comprehensive schools, Jones was an administrative assistant at a local authority training-centre and Bishop was an operative at a factory.

The Court said that the basic principles of employers' liability apply ie duty of care, breach of duty, injury caused by the breach of duty and foreseeability. This was established in *Walker v Northumberland County Council [1995] 1 All ER 737*. The Court observed the difficult areas in these cases are foreseeability (ie appreciating that the employee might suffer from stress as a result of the work he or she was doing) and finding an appropriate breach of duty that has caused the injury.

It stressed that there is a difference between psychiatric injury and occupational stress. Only if the claimant develops a psychiatric injury is there the possibility of a claim.

The Court set out 16 'practical propositions' relevant to determining liability. These are effectively the criteria cases will have to meet if they are likely to succeed. These practical propositions are as follows.

Application of the law

1   The ordinary principles of employer's liability apply.

Foreseeability

2   The employee must prove that it was **reasonably foreseeable** to his or her employer that he or she would sustain psychiatric ill health (as distinct from occupational stress) which is attributable to stress at work (as distinct from other factors).

3   Foreseeability depends upon what the employer knows (or ought reasonably to know) about the employee. An employer is usually entitled to assume that an employee can withstand the normal pressures of the job unless he knows of some particular problem or vulnerability.

4   There are no occupations that should be regarded as intrinsically dangerous to mental health.

5   Factors likely to be relevant in considering whether the employer was on notice that he needed to take action in relation to the employee's stress:

(a)   was the workload more than normal for the job;

(b)   was the work particularly demanding for this employee;

(c)   were the demands on the employee unreasonable compared to those on colleagues;

(d)   were there signs that colleagues doing the same job were suffering high levels of stress;

(e)   was there an abnormal level of sickness or absenteeism in relation to the same job or in the department where the employee worked;

(f)   were there signs from the employee of impending harm to his or her health;

(cont'd)

(g)   had the employee a particular problem or vulnerability;

(h)   had the employee already suffered an illness related to stress at work;

(i)   prior to the employee's psychiatric illness had the employee recently had frequent or prolonged absence from work which was uncharacteristic; and

(j)   were there relevant complaints from the employee or others to the employer?

6   The employer is generally entitled to take what he is told by his employee at face value (unless there is good reason to think otherwise). He does not generally have to make searching enquiries of the employee or medical advisers.

7   The employer only has to take action if there are indications of impending harm to the health of the employee arising from stress at work and these must be plain enough for any reasonable employer to realise that he should do something about it.

Breach of duty

8   The employer is only in breach of duty if he has failed to take reasonably practicable steps to prevent the harm caused by the work stress.

9   The size and scope of the employer's operation, its resources and the demands it faces are relevant in deciding what is reasonable (this includes the effect upon other employees).

10   An employer can only reasonably be expected to take steps that are likely to do some good: the court is likely to need expert evidence on this.

11   An employer who offers a confidential advice service, with referral to appropriate counselling or treatment services, is unlikely to be found in breach of duty.

12   If the only reasonable and effective step would have been to dismiss or demote the employee, the employer will not be in breach of duty in allowing a willing employee to continue in the job.

13   In all cases it is necessary to identify the steps that the employer both could and should have taken before finding him in breach of his duty of care.

Causation

14   The employee must show that a **breach of duty** has caused or materially contributed to the psychiatric illness. It is not enough to show that

work on its own has caused the illness. It must be linked to a breach of duty by the employer.

Apportionment and quantification

15   Where the psychiatric illness suffered has more than one cause, the employer should only pay for that proportion of the caused by his breach of duty, unless the harm is truly indivisible. It is for the defendant to raise the question of apportionment.

16   The assessment of damages will take account of any pre-existing disorder or vulnerability and of the chance that the employee would have succumbed to a stress related disorder in any event.

The Judgement refers to the HSE guidance published in 1995 on stress. By the time the Court of Appeal heard the appeals this had been updated with the 2001 publication *Tackling work-related stress*. This later publication makes it quite clear that the HSE expects employers to apply the normal procedures of risk assessment as required by *Regulation 3* of the *Management of Health and Safety at Work Regulations 1999 (SI 1999 No 3242)*.

The case of *Cross v Hyland Enterprise [2001] IRLR 336* is often cited as authority for saying there is no duty for an employer to risk assess stress. However the case related to a stress condition that arose in 1993 (the requirement to carry out general risk became effective in January 1993 under *SI 1999 No 3242* and the court made it clear that it expressed no view on the current state of employers' knowledge as at the time the case was heard in December 2000.

Although the Court does not specifically deal with issue of risk assessment, in a sense another way of looking at what the Court has said is to say:

• is there a hazard in the workplace that might give rise to stress, which the employer should have been aware of; and

• if so, would a suitable and sufficient risk assessment have shown that a possible danger of the hazard was an employee suffering a psychiatric illness?

However the overriding message of the Court of Appeal is that employees should complain to their employers about their problems so that the employer is on notice. In other words, the employee should not have suffered in silence. Having said this there will be certain circumstances where even without complaints, employers will be expected to take action, for example if the employee has a vulnerability which the employer is aware of.

For example the employer might be aware of an employee's vulnerability when they return from illness unconnected with work. This was the position in the case *Witham v Hastings & Rother NHS Trust* (4 October 2001, unreported) *QB (Rex Tedd QC)* (but note decided prior to the Hatton Judgement). This stress claim was brought by a senior nurse against her former employer. In 1995, whilst a grade G nursing sister, she suffered an episode of post-natal depression. She was off for eight months and agreed to return to work in March 1996. The defendant promised the return to work would be gradual and there would be a lot of support. This did not happen and her mental health deteriorated. She was successful in her claim as the defendant failed to manage her return to work having been on notice of her condition.

In *Walker v Northumberland County Council [1995] 1 All ER 737* the claimant, a social worker, had two nervous breakdowns. However he only recovered compensation for the second breakdown. Although his employers were on notice they continued to over burden him.

The Court in the appeal cases said that the impending harm must be 'plain enough for any reasonable employer to realise that he should do something about it' (see practical proposition 7). This seems to suggest that the employer can just sit back and wait and see what happens. Such an interpretation of what the Court is saying would arguably be setting the trigger point too low. Once a hazard is apparent the employer must risk assess it and evaluate the risk. Practical proposition six says that the employer is generally entitled to take what he is told by his employee at face value. However this must be subject, as appropriate, to the requirements of a suitable and sufficient risk assessment.

The Court of Appeal suggestion that an employer who offers a confidential advice service, with referral to appropriate counselling or treatment services is unlikely to be found to be in breach of duty (practical proposition 11) should be treated with caution. This part of the judgement does not fit well with *SI 1999 No 3242, Reg 4*. The priority control measure must surely be to treat the risk at source not to just look for mitigation.

It is also suggested that the Court of Appeal's practical proposition number twelve must be treated with caution, particularly in relation to the *Disability Discrimination Act 1995*.

On 1 April 2004 the House of Lords overturned the Court of Appeal decision in respect of Barber. By the time the matter reached the Lords, Barber had abandoned his criticisms of the Court of Appeal's guidelines. The Lords followed these principles and reinstated the decision of the first instance judge.

On a number of occasions Barber had brought his symptoms to the attention of his head teacher, but no action was taken to deal with his workload. The Lords effectively ruled that Barber had done enough to come within the terms of the guidelines to show there had been a breach of duty by his employers.

Back injuries 4.10

Many back injuries occur when employees lift something as part of their job. These types of accidents are covered by the *Manual Handling Operations Regulations 1992 (MHOR) (SI 1992 No 2793)*.

A 'manual handling operation' is defined in *SI 1992 No 2793, Reg 2* as:

'any transporting, or supporting of a load (including the lifting, putting down, pushing, pulling, carrying or moving thereof) by hand or by bodily force'.

Therefore a manual handling operation can range from someone having to lift a heavy box at work to someone working on the production line at a factory, packing chicken meat.

In a nutshell, if there is a risk of injury from a manual handling operation (by reference to the requirement to carry out a general risk assessment pursuant to *Regulation 3* of the *Management of Health and Safety at Work Regulations 1999 (SI 1999 No 3242) SI 1992 No 2793* requires the employer to *avoid manual handling with a risk of injury*, so far as is reasonably practicable. If that is not reasonably practicable, *a risk assessment should be carried out and measures put in place to reduce the risk to the lowest level reasonably practicable* (see *SI 1992 No 2793, Reg 4*).

It must be remembered there is a continuing duty. It is not enough for the employer to make changes to manual handling operations and then hope the problem has been solved. Steps to avoid manual handling or to reduce the risk of injury have to be monitored, and if they are not working, alternative measures have to be sought.

SI 1992 No 2793, Reg 4 was amended by the *Health and Safety (Miscellaneous Amendments) Regulations 2002 (SI 2002 No 2174)* to include factors that need to be taken into account when carrying out a risk assessment. These are:

(a)   the physical suitability of the employee to carryout the operations;

(b)   the clothing, footwear or other personal effects he or she is wearing;

(c)   his knowledge and training;

(d)   the results of any relevant risk assessment carried out pursuant to *SI 1999 No 3242, Reg 3*;

(e)   whether the employee is within a group of employees identified by that assessment as being especially at risk; and

(f)   the results of any health surveillance provided pursuant to *SI 1999 No 3242, Reg 6*.

The first major case on *SI 1992 No 2793* to come before the Court of Appeal was *Hawkes v London Borough of Southwark* (19 February 1998, unreported). The claimant was carrying a door up a flight of stairs when he fell injuring himself. The court's approach was that as a matter of common sense this was a two man job. There were no risk assessments. The court said the requirement to carry out a risk assessment under *SI 1992 No 2793* is 'merely an exhortation with no sanction attached'. However the court's attitude to risk assessment appears to be changing.

In *O'Neil v DSG Retail Ltd [2002] All ER (D) 500* concerned a claim by a ware-houseman against his employers for a breach of *SI 1992 No 2793* for failing to reduce the risk from a lifting operation to the lowest level reasonably practicable.

The Court of Appeal said that in assessing the risk, the employers must consider the particular task, the context of where it was being performed and the employee who was to perform the task.

In *Knott v Newham Health Care NHS [2002] EWHC 2091 QB* a nurse succeeded in her compensation claim when inadequate lifting equipment in a London hos-pital left her with permanent back injury so severe that she was warned not to have children. (The employers appealed. The Court of Appeal upheld the deci-sion on 13 May 2003).

Knott suffered a disc prolapse and neural damage through lifting patients over a long period of time. The trial judge found the hospital had made no risk assess-ment before March 1998, nor had they taken appropriate steps to reduce the risk of injury. Arrangements for lifting were inadequate to protect staff. The 'drag lift' was habitually used to move patients, while there was only one hoist which could be used by two wards. The judge held that the lifting significantly loaded Knott's lumber spine and advanced the likelihood of disc protrusion.

The case of *Wells v West Hertfordshire Health Authority [2000] 6 CL 329* is interest-ing with respect to the issue of capabilities. The claimant was a midwife with 28 years experience working in a delivery suit of a hospital. The work involved heavy manual handling of patients. The claimant had a history of back problems. Her employers did not send her to its occupational health department to assess her fitness for the work despite knowing of her problems. Due to the work she aggra-vated her back condition. Her claim for compensation succeeded. The court found:

- *SI 1992 No 2793* applied to the work;

- the employer failed to carry out a risk assessment pursuant to *SI 1992 No 2793*;

- the employer failed to carry out an assessment of the claimant's capabilities to do the work pursuant to *SI 1992 No 2793*;

- the employer was in breach of its statutory requirements and also negligent;

- the work accelerated the claimant's back condition by two years; and

- the claimant was not contributory negligent.

RSI 4.11

According to the HSE more than one million people are suffering from work related musculoskeletal disorders including RSI making it the most common form of work related ill health.

RSI is used to describe a group of musculoskeletal disorders such as tenosynovitis, carpal tunnel syndrome and tennis elbow that have been caused by work as a result of repetitive movements or over-use. It has also become used as a term to describe a chronic pain syndrome, with a variety of symptoms, also resulting from repetitive work, sometimes referred to as 'diffuse RSI'. It is diffuse RSI that has become the most contentious issue in these types of claims and has been the subject of the most recent cases.

Thus the legal and medical view is that RSI is a generic term used to describe a number of different conditions. There are a number of other terms that are used in addition to RSI in a generic way, such as repetitive strain syndrome and work related upper limb disorder (WRULD).

Workers that suffer from RSI broadly fall into two main groups: 'factory' workers and 'office' workers.

Factory workers usually work on production lines doing things like rapid packing or chicken trussing. Their work involves repeated rapid movements that do not necessarily involve heavy loads or long periods of time.

Office workers use computer keyboards and include such jobs as secretaries and journalists. Their condition often arises from continuous muscle contraction caused by a person holding a fixed position while their limbs are unsupported.

The Government has set targets in relation to RSI as part the HSC's *Securing health together (MISC 225 (2000))* to be achieved by 2010. These are:

- 20 per cent reduction in the incidence of RSI; and

- 30 per cent reduction in the number or working days lost through RSI.

Tenosynovitis was made a prescribed disease in 1948. There was no guidance as to the risk of RSI (in factory cases) and how it could be avoided until the early 1970s. The risk of tenosynovitis for repetitive work was set out in the guidance note of 1972 by the Employers' Medical Advisory Service. The relevant parts of this note were published by the HSE in 1977 in the note MS10. There was a further Guidance published by the HSE *Work Related Upper Limb Disorder – A Guide to Prevention* (HSG60 first published in 1990).

The guidance in relation to keyboard work did not start appearing until the 1980s. In 1983 the HSE published *Visual Display Units* and in 1986 *Working with Display Units*. In 1993 a Guidance was published to accompany the *Health and Safety (Display Screen Equipment) Regulations (DSE) 1992 (SI 1992 No 2792)*.

In February 2002 the HSE issued a new guidance to RSI entitled *'Upper limb disorders in the workplace'* (HSG60(rev)). This new guidance was drafted by a multi-disciplinary team of specialists in the HSE and gives general advice on the processes involved in managing RSI risks.

HSG60 (rev) reflects the changes in the understanding of risk factors and control strategies that have emerged from research over the past decade or so. This has shown the importance of psychological risk factors acting in conjunction with physical risk factors.

For example, excessive work pressure, such as high job demands, time pressures and lack of control over the pace of work can often work alongside physical risk factors and can influence both the onset and duration of symptoms.

Therefore changes in physical work environment on their own have often been found to be less effective in tackling RSI and there is increasing evidence to support an integrated management approach that addresses both organisational and physical aspects of the individual's task and work environment.

The approach set out in the guidance is:

- understand the issues and commit to action;

- create the right organisational environment;

- assess the risks of RSI in the workplace;

- reduce the risks of RSI;

- educate and inform the workforce;

- manage any episode of RSI; and

- carry out regular checks on programme effectiveness.

In February 2003 a new guidance to *SI 1992 No 2792* was published. It takes into account the huge technological changes that have taken place since the regulations came into force.

The guidance redefines what display screen equipment is covered by *SI 1992 No 2792*. It now extends beyond computers to screens used in work with TV or film pictures, and non-electronic display screens (eg microfiche readers). The guidance identifies some display screen equipment users. These not only include the obvious like data-input workers and typists, but also microelectonics assembly (where display screen equipment is often used), TV editing technicians and security control operatives.

The guidance contains advice on home workers, agency workers, risk assessments, taking breaks from using the equipment, laptops, alternative devices, health effect, prevention and rehabilitation.

The existence of a duty of care between an employee and employer can be taken for granted (see *Wilsons & Clyde Coal Co Ltd v English [1938] AC 57*). The issue is whether the employer has breached that duty by failing to take reasonable steps to protect his employees ie failed to put in place reasonably practicable control measures to prevent employees suffering from an RSI condition from doing the work.

In 2002 the HSE published a research report by Loughborough University (010) entitled *How the Courts are interpreting HSE guidance and health and safety regulations*. It states regarding the courts approach to the regulations:

> 'While the 1992 Regulations undoubtedly imposed considerable changes in the way employers were obliged to deal with the risks of [RSI], as yet there is little evidence about how they have influenced the Courts' interpretation of an employer's duty of care in claims for [RSI].'

In relation to HSE guidance the report says:

> 'HSE guidance documents are sometimes examined in minute detail when personal injury claims for [RSI] reach trial and considerable time has been spent in some cases examining precisely what was meant by certain parts of the [DSE Regulations and the MHOR]. Courts sometimes rely heavily on HSE guidance documents to assist in determining what a prudent employer should have known, but jealously guard the right to determine how Regulations should be interpreted and what constitutes an "injury" in a legal sense. Anecdotal evidence suggests that, in the context of personal injury claims for [RSI], in some cases the Courts' interpretations of certain health and safety regulations and what constitutes an "injury" in a legal sense might not be entirely consistent with what might reasonably be expected, by a lay person, reading HSE guidance.'

In the RSI case of *Lindsay & Johnson v Claremont Garments Ltd, Newcastle upon Tyne County Court* (January 1998) WRULD DB (decided before a breach of *Regulation 3* of the *Management of Health and Safety at Work Regulations (MHSWR) 1999 (SI 1999 No 3242)* gave rise to a civil action for employees) the trial judge made the following observation:

> ' ... although the absence of a necessary risk assessment is not in itself actionable as a breach of statutory duty, it is so central to the whole system that it should be considered important evidence of a failure to provide a safe system of work in all the circumstances, and therefore amount to negligence'.

The following control measures have been considered by the courts.

Warnings

In *Presland v G W Padley Ltd* (1979) unreported, Tudor-Evans J stated that an employer is under a duty in cases where the nature of the work carries *'an inherent specific and not insignificant risk'* of an employee developing an industrial disease or condition, to tell the employee at the beginning of the employment about the risk in order to allow the employee the option whether to take the job or not.

Job rotation

This is applicable to factory cases where each employee can do (theoretically) a number of different jobs on the production line. The question is whether rotation will reduce the risk. In the *Mountenay and others v Bernard Matthews Plc [1994] MLR 293* case some of the claimants succeeded on the basis the employers had failed to provide a system of job rotation.

Work rates

In factory cases the matters to be considered include the speed of the line, the hand movements involved, the length of the shift and the number of breaks and lengths of breaks in the shift. As to what is reasonable will depend on the type of work. Relevant to the issue of work rates will be any job rotation involved in the work.

Ergonomics

Ergonomics is the study of work and its environment and conditions in order to avoid excessive fatigue, discomfort, or stress and achieve maximum efficiency and productivity. Many workstations are designed (or rather just put together) for the benefit of the work and the space that the employer has available for the work station. The employee is usually the last to be considered.

There is little doubt that the ergonomics of the workstation is something that has to be risk assessed.

In *Mughal v Reuters [1993] IRLR 571*, a VDU RSI case of a sub-editor, which was not covered by *SI 1992 No 2792*, Prosser J ruled that where employees were reasonably comfortable in their working position and where the equipment complied with the relevant British Standard there was little more that an employer could do.

Response to symptoms

When an employer is made aware that an employee has developed an RSI condition whilst working the employer should advise the employee to seek medical advice and also, if appropriate, that the condition may be work related.

However it may be argued that there is no duty upon an employer to provide alternative work relying on the case of *Withers v Perry Chain Co Ltd [1961] 3 AER*. However this must be viewed in the context of the *Disability Discrimination Act 1995*.

Supervision and training

The employer has to tell the employee of the risk and to ensure that the employee is aware of the control measures required that the risk assessment has revealed. Also it is important that employees are aware of advice in the relevant HSE publications.

In the *Mountenay* case the Judge stated that there should be an adequate period of proper training at a slow pace of work to allow the employee to become used to the type of work. The judge said the employers were under a duty to *'effect a gradual introduction'* to the work which carried a risk of RSI.

In the VDU case of *McSherry v BT Plc* (1991) unreported, the Judge said that employees should be advised of the importance of good posture and a good workstation.

In terms of statutory duty, in relation to factory cases it will be necessary to consider *SI 1992 No 2793*. In relation to office cases *SI 1992 No 2792* will be relevant.

SI 1992 No 2792, Reg 2 is a specific duty to carryout a risk assessment of the workstation.

SI 1992 No 2792, Reg 3 states that the workstation must satisfy certain requirements. These are set out in the schedule to the regulations. *SI 1992 No 2792, Reg 4* imposes a duty to plan that the activities of users at work so that their daily work on display screen equipment is periodically interrupted by breaks all changes of activity to reduce work load in that environment.

Gallagher v Bond Pearce (2001) unreported, saw the claimant awarded compensation of just over £85,000 for diffuse RSI. The claimant established breaches of *Regulations 2, 3* and *4* of *SI 1992 No 2792* which were causative of her condition.

COSHH   4.12

The *Control of Substances Hazardous to Health Regulations (COSHH) 2002 (SI 2002 No 2677)* are very detailed. The original *COSHH Regulations* of 1988 (*Control of Substances Hazardous to Health Regulations (COSHH) (SI 1988 No 1657)*) introduced for the first time to English law the concept of risk assessment. In brief *COSHH* requires:

- carrying out risk assessments of *SI 2002 No 2677* substances;

- working out the control measures required;

- ensuring the control measures are effective;

- monitoring the exposure of employees;

- providing information, training and supervision as necessary; and

- regular review of the assessments and their validity in the light of experience.

A substance which is hazardous to health includes any material, mixture or compound used at work or arising from work activities, that is harmful to a person's health in the form in which it occurs in the work activity.

Pursuant to *SI 2002 No 2677, Reg 6*, an employer MUST NOT carry on any work which is liable to expose any employee to a substance hazardous to health UNLESS a suitable and sufficient assessment has been made of the risk to health created by the substance at work and about the measures necessary to control exposure to it.

SI 2002 No 2677, Reg 7, deals with an employer's duty in relation to the prevention or control of exposure of employees to hazardous substances.

SI 2002 No 2677, Reg 7(1) says:

> 'Every employer shall ensure that the exposure of his employees to a substance hazardous to health is either prevented or, where this is not reasonably practicable, adequately controlled.'

The term 'adequate' is defined by *SI 2002 No 2677, Reg 7(11)* as follows:

> 'In this regulation "adequate" means adequate having regard only to the nature of the substance and the nature and degree of exposure to substances hazardous to health and "adequately" shall be construed accordingly.'

The case of *Dugmore v Swansea NHS Trust [2003] 1 All ER 333*, is important to the interpretation of *SI 2002 No 2677, Reg 7(1)*. The Court of Appeal considered *SI 1988 No 1657, Reg 7(1)*, which has the same wording as the current Regulations. This was a claim for compensation for personal injuries. One of the questions before the court was: what is the extent of an employer's duty under this provision and in particular to what extent is their knowledge of the risk relevant to that duty?

The claimant was a nurse and had worked in health care from leaving school. Since a baby she had suffered from eczema and asthma. During her time at Singleton Hospital, run by the Trust, she developed a Type I allergy to latex protein as a result of using powdered latex gloves in the course of her work. This happened in around 1994. It was common ground between the parties that latex was a substance hazardous to health within the meaning of *SI 2002 No 2677*.

The court said *SI 2002 No 2677, Reg 7(1)* uses the language of strict liability in providing that an employer 'shall ensure' that exposure is either prevented or controlled. The primary duty is to prevent exposure altogether, unless this is not reasonably practicable.

If prevention is not reasonably practicable, the secondary duty is to adequately control the exposure. The only relevant factors to this duty, the court confirmed, are the nature of the substance and the nature and degree of exposure generally.

The Court rejected the Trust's argument that the defence of reasonable practicability applied not only to prevention but also to the duty to adequately control exposure. It pointed out the secondary duty had no reference to reasonableness.

But is an employer only required to comply with the Regulation if the employer can reasonably foresee the risk? The court's answer to this was 'no'.

The employer has an absolute duty to protect employees from substances hazardous to health. The court pointed out there is no reference in the regulation to the foreseeability of the risk. Thus, in determining whether an employer is in breach, it is irrelevant whether or not a risk assessment (pursuant to *SI 2002 No 2677, Reg 6*) would have revealed the risk.

In the trial at the county court the judge dismissed the claimant's case. The Court of Appeal overturned this decision. The court said the exposure could have been avoided by providing the claimant with vinyl gloves. The onus was on Trust to prove that it was not reasonably practicable for them to do this.

If the Trust could have shown this, then the question was whether the exposure was adequately controlled. In relation to this the Court of Appeal concluded:

> 'It cannot be adequate control to oblige an employee frequently to wear powdered latex gloves when other barriers are available.'

There can be no confusion over the court's interpretation of *SI 2002 No 2677, Reg 7(1)*. Employers have to take reasonably practicable steps to avoid exposure to employees of hazardous substances.

If this cannot be done, then adequate control measures must be put in place. As to what is adequate depends on the substance and the nature and extent of the exposure. An employer cannot escape liability by arguing that he took reasonably practicable steps to control the exposure or that the risks of exposure were not reasonably foreseeable.

This case is likely to have a significant impact upon employers in relation to *SI 2002 No 2677* and occupational health considerations.

SI 2002 No 2677, Reg 10 requires monitoring of employees to be carried out where it is necessary to ensure the exposure is adequately controlled. For listed processes and substances, the frequency is specified. Records for this monitoring have to be kept for at least five years, or 40 years where the employees can be personally identified. Monitoring is required where:

- there could be serious risks to health if control measures should deteriorate; and

- it cannot be guaranteed without measurement that exposure limits are not being exceeded, or control measures are working properly.

SI 2002 No 2677, Reg 11 requires health surveillance where appropriate, which would be where there is a significant exposure to a substance listed in *SI 2002 No 2677, Sch 6* and the employee is working at a process specified or:

- where there is an identifiable disease or adverse health effect which may be related to the exposure;

- there is a reasonable likelihood that this may occur under the particular work conditions; and

- there are valid techniques for detecting indications of it.

The surveillance can be done by nurses, doctors or trained supervisors. The records have to be kept for 40 years.

Employment Rights Act 1996   4.13

The *Employment Rights Act 1996 (ERA 1996)* is the main piece of legislation covering employment rights and contains the important provisions in respect of unfair dismissal and redundancy. The most relevant legislation in respect of employment rights and rehabilitation is the *Disability Discrimination Act 1995 (DDA 1995)* which is dealt with below. Complaints under the *ERA 1996* and *DDA 1995* are made to an employment tribunal. There is a time limit of three months to lodge the complaint. Often a complaint regarding disability discrimination will be made in conjunction with an unfair dismissal claim.

The *Employment Act 2002* sets out statutory dismissal and disciplinary procedures and grievance procedures. The idea is to encourage more resolution of employment disputes without recourse to employment tribunals. These procedures are expected to come into force in October 2004.

Unfair dismissal   4.14

Dismissal is the termination of employment. Most employees have the right to complain of unfair dismissal to an employment tribunal but there are certain exceptions. The main qualifications are that the employee must not be of retirement age and must have at least twelve months continuous employment (this qualification is reduced to four weeks where an employee is dismissed on medical grounds in consequence of certain health and safety requirements or recommendations).

Dismissal will only be fair if the employer can show that the reason was one of those listed below and the employer acted reasonably in the circumstances (including the size and administrative resources of the business) in treating that reason as sufficient to justify dismissal.

The reasons are:

- reason related to the employee's capability or qualification for the job;

- reason related to the employee's conduct;

- redundancy (though in certain circumstances the selection for redundancy can be unfair);

- statutory restriction on either the employer or the employee which prevents the employment being continued; and

- some other substantial reason that could justify the dismissal.

Where an employment tribunal finds someone has been unfairly dismisses it can order reinstatement or re-engagement. Alternatively the tribunal may award compensation.

Redundancy   4.15

An employee will be entitled to a payment under the *Employment Rights Act 1996* only if the reason for his or her dismissal is redundancy. This means that the dismissal must be caused by the employer's need to reduce the workforce. Normally the job must have disappeared. It is not redundancy if the employer immediately takes on a direct replacement for the person. But it will not matter if the employer is recruiting more workers for work of a different kind, or in another location.

To qualify for redundancy the employee must have a contract of employment, have two years continuous employment and not be of retirement age.

Medical suspension pay   4.16

Under the *Employment Rights Act 1996, s 64* an employee who is suspended from work on certain specified medical grounds is entitled to receive medical suspension pay for up to 26 weeks of suspension. This applies where the employee is suspended because of a requirement imposed by statute or due to any provision of code of practice issues pursuant to the *Health and Safety at Work etc. Act 1974*.

Disability Discrimination Act 1995   4.17

The *Disability Discrimination Act 1995 (DDA 1995) (Part II)* makes it unlawful for an employer to discriminate against a disabled job applicant or worker in:

- recruitment;

- terms and conditions of employment;

- promotion or transfer;

- training;

- employment benefits; and

- dismissal or any other detrimental treatment.

In terms of recruitment, discrimination can occur in the arrangements the employer makes for deciding whom should be offered employment, the terms on which employment is offered or by the employer refusing, or not offering, a person with a disability employment.

In respect of a person with a disability already working for the employer, discrimination can occur in the terms upon which that person is employed, the opportunities given to that person for promotion, transfer, training or receiving any other benefit, facility or service or by refusing to that person any of these opportunities or deliberately not offering them.

The Act in addition to covering employees it also covers the self-employed, temporary and contract workers.

From the 1 October 2004 the *Disability Discrimination Act 1995 (Amendment) Regulations 2003 (SI 2003 No 1673)* (which are in response to the *Framework Employment Directive 2000/78/EC*) removes the small firm exemption that applies to employers with fewer than 15 staff. Small employers have not been required to meet the employment provisions of *DDA 1995*. The new regulations also remove the *DDA 1995* exemption from the police, fire and prison services.

Further a joint parliamentary committee is working on the Draft Disability Discrimination Bill. This has recommended that the new Bill should allow employment tribunals to re-instate disabled employees in disability discrimination cases.

There are Notes of Guidance and a Code of Practice to *DDA 1995* (a new code will come into effect as from October 2004) that accompany the Act.

Definition of disability   4.18

Under *Disability Discrimination Act 1995 (DDA 1995), s 1* a disability means a physical or mental impairment that has a substantial and long-term adverse effect on a person's ability to carry out their normal day-to-day activities. In other words the physical or mental impairment must be the cause of the substantial and long-term adverse effects.

There is no definition in the Act of impairment. The guidance to *DDA 1995* states that mental impairment is one resulting from a mental illness that is clinically well recognised. The *Disability and Discrimination (Meaning of Disability) Regulations 1996 (SI 1996 No 1455)* list conditions to be treated as amounting to an impairment.

DDA 1995, Sch 1 defines 'long term' as referring to an impairment which has lasted, or which is likely to last, for at least either twelve months or for the rest of the person's life. Recurrent conditions may also qualify as disabilities provided they are likely to reoccur at least every twelve months. This would include for example epilepsy.

Schedule 1 also lists the day-to-day activities that the impairment must adversely effect for a person to be disabled under the *DDA 1995*. These are:

- mobility;
- manual dexterity;
- physical co-ordination;
- continence;
- ability to lift, carry or otherwise move everyday objects;
- speech, hearing, eyesight;
- memory or the ability to concentrate, learn or understand; or
- the perception of the risk of physical danger.

The Guidance to the *DDA 1995* gives examples of effects that would amount to an impairment and those that would not.

For an impairment to come within the Act, it is important to note that the severity of it is not the issue, but whether it has a *substantial* effect upon day-to-day activities. Thus, for example, someone suffering from cancer would not come within the Act unless the illness had a substantial effect upon his or her normal day-to-day activities. Also, a person may have a number of impairments which on their own would not have a substantial effect. However, if the impairments taken together have a substantial effect upon day-to-day activities, then the Act will apply.

The time taken to carry out tasks and the way in which tasks are carried out are relevant to considering the effect the impairment has. Environmental conditions (eg temperature and humidity) are relevant to considering if the impairment has a substantial adverse effect. When assessing the effects of an impairment, medical treatment or other aid used to treat or correct the impairment may not be taken into account (except that is for glasses and contact lenses in relation to sight).

Discrimination   4.19

Disability Discrimination Act 1995 (DDA 1995), s 5(1) states an employer discriminates against a disabled person if, for a reason that relates to his or her disability, the employer:

- treats him or her less favourably than it treats, or would treat, others to whom that reason does not, or would not, apply; and
- cannot show that treatment is justified.

DDA 1995 does not require an employer to have knowledge of a person's disability for discrimination to occur. In *Clark v Novacold [1999] IRLR 318* the Court of Appeal said that the test for less favourable treatment was based on the reason for the treatment of the disabled person, not the fact of his or her disability. This suggested an employer could discriminate against a disabled person if unaware of his or her disability.

In *Heinz v Kenrick [2000] IRLR 144* the applicant suffered form chronic fatigue syndrome which was diagnosed after he was dismissed. The Employment Appeals Tribunal (EAT) held that the employer could still be liable under the Act even though not aware of the disability. However it was added that the absence of knowledge of the disability might be highly material to the issue of justification or the employers' duty to make reasonable adjustments pursuant to *DDA 1995, s 6*.

In *Reedman v French Connection Ltd* (1997) unreported the employment tribunal said that once it was established the person was disabled and a *prima facie* case had been proved of less favourable treatment it was for the employer to give an explanation. If the explanation is inadequate then the tribunal may infer that the less favourable treatment was because of the person's disability.

It should be noted as from October 2004 the rule will be that where a complainant proves facts upon which the employment tribunal may conclude, in the absence of an adequate explanation, that the respondent has acted in a way which is unlawful under the employment provisions, the tribunal must uphold the complaint unless the respondent employer proves that it did not act in this way.

Usual grounds put forward for justification are the extent of sick leave taken by the employee, his or her capacity to perform his or her job and health and safety concerns arising from the employer continuing to employ the employee.

The Court of Appeal decision in *Jones v Post Office [2001] IRLR 384* confirmed that the threshold for the justification defence is low. The case also established that if an employer relies upon a risk assessment, when justification relates to health and safety grounds, then an employment tribunal may not substitute its own assessment in place of the employer's.

The case concerned a driver of a mail delivery van who was diagnosed with mature onset diabetes. This was initially treated by diet but when he became insulin dependent he was removed from driving duties. The Post Office reviewed the position and offered to allow him to perform driving duties for up to two hours in a 24-hour period. This was not acceptable to him.

The employer had obtained what were admitted to be suitably qualified and expert medical opinions. The Court of Appeal ruled that where a properly conducted risk assessment provides a reason that is on the face of it both material and substantial, and it is not irrational, the employment tribunal could not substitute its own appraisal. The Court went on to say that it would be different if there was no risk assessment or a decision was taken otherwise than on the basis of appropriate medical evidence or was an irrational decision as being beyond the range of responses open to a reasonable decision maker.

The Employment Appeal Tribunal decision in *Surrey Police v Marshall [2002] IRLR 843* shows how difficult it is to challenge the decision of an occupational health doctor even where the assessment is made purely on paperwork without meeting the person with the disability or seeking the opinion from their specialist consultant.

From 1 October 2004 the 'justification' defence will no longer be available where less favourable treatment amounts to 'direct discrimination'. An employer directly discriminates against a disabled person if, on the ground of the disabled person's disability, the employer treats the disabled person less favourably than it treats (or would treat) a person not having that particular disability whose relevant circumstances, including his abilities, are the same as, or not materially different from, those of the disabled person. Where the discrimination is not direct, then the existing justification test will apply.

Reasonable adjustments 4.20

Disability Discrimination Act 1995 (DDA 1995), s 5(2) states that an employer discriminates against a person with a disability if the employer fails to provide reasonable adjustments to the working environment as required by *DDA 1995, s 6*. As from the 1 October 2004 there will be no defence of justification for failure to make reasonable adjustments (although a valid justification will be taken into account when assessing whether an adjustment is reasonable). Further the reasonable adjustment rules will be changed from applying to 'arrangements' to any 'provision, criterion or practice' applied by or on behalf of an employer. Provision, criterion or practice includes any arrangements.

DDA 1995 gives examples of reasonable steps which employers might have to take including:

- making adjustments to premises;
- allocating some of the employee's duties to another person;
- transferring the person to a vacancy;
- altering the person's working hours;
- assigning the person to a different place of work;
- allowing time off for rehabilitation, assessment or treatment;
- arranging training;
- acquiring or modifying equipment;
- providing a reader or interpreter;
- modifying instructions or reference manuals;
- modifying procedures for testing or assessment; and
- supervision.

The *Disability Discrimination Act 1995 (Amendment) Regulations 2003 (SI 2003 No 1673)* make some changes to the examples of steps that an employer may need to take to comply with the duty to make reasonable adjustments. One new additional example is arranging training for persons other than the disabled person – such as in disability issues.

The duty to make reasonable adjustments arises when the employer knows or could be reasonably expected to know, that the person has a disability and, as a consequence, is placed at a substantial disadvantage. It applies to recruitment as well as to existing employees.

In *Morse v Wiltshire County Council [1998] IRLR 352* the EAT set out two steps an employment tribunal must go through when dealing with a complaint of an employer having failed to make reasonable adjustments. First, the tribunal must decide whether the employer owed a duty pursuant to *DDA 1995, s 6*. Second, if such a duty does exist, the tribunal must decide whether or not the employer has taken such steps as are reasonable to prevent the disable person being placed at a substantial disadvantage. (It should be noted the EAT then said the tribunal should go onto to decide whether the failure was justified, but as stated above, the justification defence will no longer apply after October 2004 to the reasonable adjustments duty.)

Harassment   4.21

The *Disability Discrimination Act 1995* will specifically cover harassment from October 2004. An employer subjects a disabled person to 'harassment' where, for a reason which relates to the disabled person's disability, it engages in unwanted conduct which has the purpose or effect of (a) violating the disabled person's dignity, or (b) creating an intimidating, hostile, degrading, humiliating or offensive environment for him or her.

Conflict between the Health and Safety at Work etc. Act 1974, and the Disability Discrimination Act 1995   4.22

The HSE has published research which says that around 25 per cent of employers perceive there is a conflict between health and safety requirements and the *Disability Discrimination Act 1995 (DDA 1995)*. (The extent of use of health and safety requirements as a false excuse for not employing sick or disabled persons. HSE Research Report No 167, HSE Books, 2003, download at www.hse.gov.uk.) Concerns regarding the health and safety of people with a disability or their colleagues are sometimes used for not retaining or employing a disabled person.

The research found that employers failed to justify health and safety as a valid reason for discriminating against a disabled worker in 30 per cent of cases heard at employment tribunals and in cases relating to non retention of disabled people this rose to 40 per cent. In most cases the tribunals ruled that the employer had either failed to make an adequate risk assessment of the health and safety hazards or had failed to make reasonable adjustments to overcome the health and safety problem.

An interesting dilemma arises if the only safe course of action is to dismiss the person with a disability because of health and safety risks to him or her continuing in employment, but the person nonetheless wishes to continue. The Court of Appeal in the case of *Withers v Perry Chain Co Ltd [1961] 3 AER* (pre-DDA *1995*) concluded there was no common law duty to dismiss in these circumstances. In *Hatton v Sutherland and three other appeals [2002] PIQR P21* (see **4.9** above) the Court of Appeal followed this approach in relation to stress.

However contrast this with the Court of Appeal decision in *Coxall v Goodyear Great Britain Ltd [2002] IRLR 742*. Mr Coxall was employed to spray tyres with lubricant paint. His employer had set up a safe place of work. However, the exposure to paint caused Mr Coxall to suffer with asthma. He brought a personal injury claim against his employers for allowing him to continue to work once he had been diagnosed with asthma, even though he had wanted to carry on with the job.

The Court of Appeal held that an employer may be under a duty to stop an employee doing a job (whether by finding alternative employment or even dismissing him) regardless of the employee's own wishes, where he is at risk of injury if he continues in it. Whether or not that duty arises depends on the magnitude of the risk to the employee's health.

Lane Group PLC and North Somerset Council v Farmiloe (24 November 2003, unreported) was an appeal heard by the EAT. Mr Farmiloe worked as a warehouseman for Lane Group. He suffered from the skin condition psoriasis which meant that he was limited in the type of footwear he could wear.

In 1996 the employer carried out a risk assessment and as a consequence introduced a policy that all staff working in the warehouse must wear safety footwear. An exception was made for Mr Farmiloe who was allowed to wear his own sturdy but soft leather shoes.

A health and safety officer from the local authority carried out a routine inspection and noted that Mr Farmiloe did not wear the requisite footwear because of his skin condition. *Regulation 4* of the *Personal Protective Equipment (EC Directive) Regulations (PPE) 1992 (SI 1992 No 3139)* requires employers to provide personal protective equipment where the risks to an employee's health and safety cannot be controlled in any other way. In other words it is the option of last resort. The inspector informed the employer that an exception could not be made and recommended that a medical assessment be made to se if alternative footwear could be found. The inspector also informed the employer that as the assessment had highlighted the need for personal protective equipment, it was for the employer to ensure it was provided and worn.

The employer searched without success for alternative footwear. There was no alternative employment available that would allow Mr Farmiloe to continue in employment without having to wear safety footwear. The employer therefore dismissed Mr Farmiloe. Mr Farmiloe brought an action for discrimination against his employers and the local authority (he also brought an action for unfair dismissal against his employers but this issue was not considered by the EAT).

The EAT found that *SI 1992 No 3139* imposed an absolute duty upon the employer to provide personal protective equipment. This meant that once it was established that an employee remained exposed to a health and safety risk that could not be adequately or effectively controlled by other means, the employer must provide personal protective equipment and ensure it is worn.

The duty under *DDA 1995, s 6* to make reasonable adjustments meant that the employer must take reasonable steps to find personal protective equipment suitable for the individual. If that was not practicable the employer must find suitable alternative employment not requiring the personal protective equipment. Since there was no alternative employment available there were no further adjustments the employer could make.

On the facts the dismissal was an inevitable consequence of the employer's obligation under the *SI 1992 No 3139* and as such there had been no discrimination by either the employer or the local authority.

Working Time Regulations 1998 4.23

The European Court of Justice has determined that working time is a health and safety issue. In *UK v European Commission [1996] ECR I-5755* the Advocate-General Leger at paragraph 103 of his opinion stated that without legislation workers are exposed:

'To the risk of frequently being required to work excessively long hours beyond their physical or psychological capabilities, thereby jeopardising their health and safety.'

The *Working Time Directive (93/104/EC)* laid down rules on working hours, rest periods and holidays, but also allowed member states to implement legislation that gave employees the right to opt out. The directive also excluded certain types of employment such as transport workers, fishing and doctors.

The directive was enacted into UK law as the *Working Time Regulations 1998 (SI 1998 No 1833)*. The four principal areas covered are:

- minimum weekly working time – a worker's working time, including overtime, is not to exceed 48 hours for each seven days in any particular reference period;

- limits in night working – a night worker's normal hours of work in any reference period are not to exceed an average of eight hours in every 24 hours;

- rest periods – a minimum rest period of eleven consecutive hours for each 24-hour period and a minimum rest period of one day per week; and

- paid annual leave – a worker is entitled to four weeks paid leave in each leave year.

The Regulations are notable for their adoption of the derogations allowed by the directive. Thus an employee can agree to work more than 48 hours in a week.

An amending *Directive (2000/34/EC)* was adopted in 2000 which requires member states to cover previously excluded workers. The *Working Time (Amendment) Regulations 2003 (SI 2003 No 1684)* implemented this directive. As from the 1 August 2004 doctors in training will be limited to 58 hours per week.

The European Commission (EC) has expressed concern about the UK's implementation of the *Working Time Directive*. Two significant issues are under review:

- derogations from the reference period for the 48 hour maximum working week; and

- the option of not applying the maximum working week if the worker agrees.

The EC is considering proposals for an amending directive. Theses are not expected until the autumn of 2004 at the earliest.

There have been some prosecutions for breaching of the *Working Time Regulations 1998 (SI 1998 No 1833)*. In 2000 T&S Stores were prosecuted at Norwich Magistrates Court. The store had failed to offer to a night worker a suitable health assessment as required by the Regulations. The store was fined £400.

Medical Records, Medical Reports and Confidentiality   4.24

Medical records are records that contain a full account of everything in a patient's medical history, whereas a *medical report* is a document that contains a doctor's or consultant's response (and opinion) about certain questions that have been put to him or her. A report might be prepared in connection with the clinical care of a person or, where there is no clinical relationship eg for the purposes of legal proceedings. There are certain legal rules that govern the release and access to a person's medical records and reports.

Occupational health (OH) practitioners have a difficult task in balancing their duty to the employee and their duty to the employer. This can manifest itself in the duty of confidentiality. In October 2003 the Royal College of Nursing

(RCN) published guidelines for occupational health nurses on confidentiality, which is a good source of reference. (This can be download from the RCN's website – www.rcn.org.uk/publications/pdf/confidentiality.pdf.) Guidance is also available in the GMC's *Confidentiality, protecting and providing information*, published in September 2000 (available on the GMC's website – www.gmc-uk.org).

In order to maintain the trust of the workers, the OH practitioner must be seen to give impartial advice and not to be seen to be looking out for the sole interests of the employer. Their job is to assist the employer in fulfilling its duties under the health and safety legislation ie providing preventative medicine.

One area where confidentiality and the legal right of access to information cause confusion is in respect of OH medical records. Although these are ultimately in the physical ownership of the employer, they are in the control of the OH practitioner while he or she holds the post. Thus under normal circumstances these records will be confidential to the OH practitioner. There is no right of access to these records either by the employer of its legal advisers unless the worker has given informed consent or there is a court order.

In *Dunn v British Coal Corporation [1993] ICR 591* the Court of Appeal accepted that occupational health records were confidential between the doctor and the employee, and that where an employer was threatened with legal action by the employee, neither the employer nor its legal advisers were entitled to see the health records in the absence of the employee's consent.

Informed consent requires that the worker clearly understands what information will be handed over, to whom, for what purpose and the possible outcomes that may arise.

There are some circumstances where the duty of confidentiality can be overridden. For example under the *Public Health (Control of Diseases) Act 1984* requires the notification of certain diseases to the local authority.

Below are set out are the relevant statutes concerning OH medical records.

Access to the Medical Reports Act 1988 4.25

The *Access to Medical Reports Act 1988* is used where medical information is sought about an individual for employment or insurance purposes form a doctor who has been caring for that individual, usually a GP or specialist. There has been some confusion as to whether the Act applies to reports being sent from an OH practitioner to a manager. However these reports usually do not contain medical information and so would not be covered.

It is common for managers to request a medical report from OH practitioners on whether an employee is fit or unfit to do work. These will not reveal clinical details. But in the case of *London Borough of Hammersmith and Fulham v Farnsworth [2000] IRLR 691* it was held that as long as the job applicant or employee had given consent, the full clinical information could be given by the OH practitioner. It should be noted however that the signed consent form was headed 'Confidential to the London Borough of Hammersmith' and not 'Confidential to the OH Department'.

For OH practitioners it has been argued that there is a legal duty to protect the health of all those in the workplace, even if they have never consulted the OH professional – see *Stokes v Guest Keen [1968] 1 WLR 1776*. Thus consultations are potentially covered by the Act.

The procedure required under the Act is as follows.

1   The employer must tell the employee that it intends to ask for a medical report and obtain the employee's consent. The employee must be informed of his or her rights to withhold consent, ask for access to the report before it is supplied, to confuse consent to the report being supplied and to request amendments to the report.

2   The employee can waive his or her right to see the report and if so it can then be sent directly to the employer.

3   If the employee asks to see the report, the reporting doctor must be told of this and the employee must advise that a request for the report has been made.

4   Where the employee has requested access to the report, the doctor must not supply the report to the employer unless the employee has been given access or 21 days have expired from the date of making the application and the doctor has received no communication from the employee about the arrangements for access.

5   Access is either showing the person the report or providing a copy for a reasonable fee.

6   Even if the employee originally said he or she did not want access to the report, the employee can change his or her mind in the 21-day period.

7   When the employee has seen the report, he or she may authorise it be released or request amendments.

8   The doctor can refuse to make the amendments to the report must the doctor must allow the employee to send a statement with the report setting out his or her view.

9   The doctor must keep a copy of the report for six months, during which time the employee can request a copy

10   The doctor is not obliged to the employee any part of the medical where disclosure in his or her opinion would be likely to cause serious harm to the physical or mental health of the employee or others, would

(cont'd)

---

indicate the intentions of the doctor in respect of the doctor in respect of the individual or would be likely to reveal information about another individual.

11   In these cases, if the exemption applies to the whole report, the doctor must inform the employee in writing and cannot the report until the employee provides written consent to the release of the report unseen.

12   The Act is enforced through the county courts.

Access to the Health Records Act 1990   4.26

Access to manual health records made since 1 November 1991 was available under this Act. However it lost much of its significance with the implementation of the *Data Protection Act 1998*.

Data Protection Act 1998   4.27

The *Data Protection Act 1998* came into effect on 24 October 2001. It relates to both computerised and manual records.

The Act strengthens the controls around the processing (collection, storage, use and disclosure) of data. It applies to data that is processed automatically and paper based systems held in relevant filing systems, such as OH record. Occupational health practitioners must make sure when processing information they do not breach the Act.

The Act introduces new definitions:

- **Personal data** – data that relates to a living person who can be identified from the data or from the data and other information which is in the possession of, or likely to come into the possession of, the data controller.

- **Data subject** – the person who is the subject of the data.

- **Data controller** – people who (either alone or jointly or in common with other people) determines the purpose for which any personal data is, or is to be, stored.

- **Data processor** – people who obtain, record or hold the data or carry out any operations or set of operations on the data.

- **On computer** – the term 'computer' is used to describe any type of computer however described.

- **Sensitive data** – includes information as to a person's 'physical or mental health or condition' and 'sexual life'.

People have the right to know why information is collected and that the data is only used for the stated purpose. They also have the right of access under the Act to personal data held on them.

Personal data must be processed fairly and lawfully. In the case of sensitive data it can be processed only if certain conditions are met. OH practitioners may process health records with the consent of the patient and in some other situations, like disclosure to other members of the health care team on a 'need-to-know' basis.

The definition of medical purposes includes:

- preventative medicine;

- medical diagnosis by a health professional;

- medical research; and

- the provision of care and treatment (although 'care' is not defined in the Act).

There are cases where exceptionally, information may be withheld from the data subject and fall within the *Data Protection (Subject Access Modification)(Health) Order 2000 (SI 2000 No 413)*. For example if the data subject's (or someone else's) physical or mental health is likely to suffer serious harm if access is given.

In relation to employment issues, the RCN guidance gives the following advice:

> 'How [OH] practitioners use information gathered during pre and post-employment screening should be given serious consideration. Data can only be used for the purposes for which it was given. Therefore, it is likely that OH practitioners may be in breach of the Act if, for example, they used data collected on pre-employment selection questionnaires for post-employment monitoring or research. This is because it is unlikely that the individual has given consent to use such data for multiple purposes. Practitioners are advised to consult the website of the Information Commissioner for up to date advice on the application of the Act to the processing of health data in an employment setting.'

In 2004 the latest section of the Information Commissioner's data protection code on *Information about workers' health* will be published. A public consultation on a draft was concluded in February 2004 (available at: www.informationcommissioner.gov.uk). The document deals with sensitive data about workers' physical or mental health. This can include information recorded as part of their sickness records, information gained at medical examination or from pre-employment questionnaires, information about an individual's disabilities, and data from workplace health surveillance.

Human Rights Act 1998 4.28

The *Human Rights Act 1998 (HRA 1998)* came into force on 2 October 2000. The Act 'gives further effect to' the European Convention for the protection of Human Rights and Fundamental Freedoms (ECHR) in domestic law:

HRA 1998 has been given partial effect since 22 May 1999, in Scotland, by virtue of the *Scotland Act 1998*. As a result of *HRA 1998*, ECHR rights can now be directly relied upon, argued and enforced in the UK courts and tribunals at all levels. The acts or omissions of 'public authorities' can be challenged as part of any legal proceedings, by judicial review or as an entirely new course of action under the Act. A public authority includes courts tribunals and any person certain of whose functions are functions of a public nature. This includes the NHS and in certain circumstances private companies that perform a public service, eg Network Rail.

It should be remembered that once all domestic remedies have been exhausted in the domestic courts, an appeal still lies to the European Court of Human Rights in Strasbourg. Decisions of the European Court of Human Rights are final and binding on member states.

A breach of confidential is likely to be a breach the UK's obligation under Article 8 of the ECHR which guarantees the right to respect for private life. In *Z v Finland [1998] 25 EHRR 371*, the European Court stated:

> 'The protection of personal data, not least personal data, not least medical data, is of fundamental importance to a person's enjoyment of his or her right to respect for private and family life as guaranteed by Article 8 of the Convention. Respecting confidentiality of health data is a vital principle in the legal systems of all contracting parties to the Convention. It is crucial not only to respect the privacy of the patient but also to preserve his or her confidence in the medical profession and in the health services in general.'

Case study 7

Mrs Smith has been a secretary for a large electronics company for six years. Her hours of work are 9am to 5pm. However she often gets into work early or leaves late in order to be able to cope with her workload. This has been the case since the secretarial support in her department was reduced from four secretaries to three 18 months ago. She calculates that she spends up to 90 per cent of her time typing at her computer.

The last time her workstation was risk assessed was two years ago and since then her workstation has changed since an office refurbishment.

Twelve months ago she went off sick with severe pains in her right. These pains had come on gradually. Prior to going off sick she had consulted the occupational health physician who had recommended that she should try to take regular breaks away from the keyboard.

She was diagnosed by a consultant as suffering from a condition called *fibromyalgia*, often referred to as a defuse RSI, in her right hand. She is right handed. Mrs Smith was off work for three months during which time her condition improved greatly. On return to work her typing duties were significantly reduced. But after six weeks her workload had almost returned to its original level. Within a month her condition was severe again and Mrs Smith has been off work ever since. Her consultant says her condition will last at least twelve months. She now has difficulty lifting objects and her husband has been doing all the ironing and shopping as a result.

On the advice of her union representative she has put in a claim against her employers for personal injuries Her boss saw a copy of the letter of claim three weeks ago. He has put pressure on the company's occupational health physician to send him a copy of her medical records because he does not think the claim is justified. The OH physician refused. A week ago Mrs Smith's boss wrote to her saying that because of her sickness record (she had been absent from work four months just over two years ago for depression) he was terminating her employment.

Comment

The relevant health and safety regulations are the *Health and Safety (Display Screen Equipment) Regulations (DSE)1992 (SI 1992 No 2792)*. It would appear there has been a breach of *SI 1992 No 2792, Reg 2* to risk assess the workstation and *SI 1992 No 2792, Reg 4* in relation to taking regular breaks. There may be an issue as to how the employers responded to her returning to work by increasing her workload so quickly. It is not clear if this was done in consultation with the OH department.

This could have been a situation where rehabilitation may have been of assistance, either in terms of medical treatment and/or altering her work in order to accommodate her condition.

Mrs Smith appears to be disabled within the terms of the *Disability Discrimination Act 1995 (DDA 1995)*. As such she may bring a discrimination claim and an unfair dismissal claim. Under the terms of the Act her employers also had a duty to provide reasonable adjustments to her work. As from October 2004 the defence of justification will no longer be a defence to failure to make reasonable adjustments.

In relation to the request for the medical records from the OH physician, these cannot be provided without either the consent of Mrs Smith or a court order.

Checklist – compliance

The following list is by no means exhaustive.

☐ Have in place a policy and procedures on rehabilitation.

☐ Have a policy and procedures on sickness absence.

☐ Ensure there is guidance on medical confidentiality.

☐ Consider the benefits of purchasing occupational health support.

☐ Check which specific health and safety legislation applies to your business in addition to the *Health and Safety at Work etc. Act 1974* and the *Management of Health and Safety at Work Regulations 1999 (SI 1999 No 3242).*

☐ Check that risk assessments are carried out not only in relation to the workplace hazards but also in relation to individuals where appropriate and that the recommended control measures are followed through. Ensure there is a system for these risk assessments to be reviewed.

☐ Ensure that risk assessment are carried out by competent persons pursuant to *SI 1999 No 3242, Reg 7.*

☐ Check that health and safety risks in relation to disability are not being used as a 'false' excuse whether by risk assessment or other justification.

☐ Consider the arrangements for health surveillance where appropriate.

☐ Consider your policies with respect to the recruitment and retention of disabled staff and that these are compliant with the *DDA 1995.* Consideration should be given to the procedures in relation to providing reasonable adjustments.

☐ Check that procedures are in place for compliance with the *Working Time Regulations 1998 (SI 1998 No 1833).*

Chapter 5
Attendance Management

Introduction

Managing attendance and absence is one of the most challenging functions of any HR manager, and is also a very important responsibility for line managers. Both short-term and long-term sickness absences can substantially damage an organisation's efficiency, injure morale and cost large amounts of money. It is therefore very important for managers to acquire the knowledge and skills to deal firmly, but also sympathetically, with employees who are, or have been sick, irrespective of whether the absences consist of frequent short periods of non-attendance, or a single lengthy period of absence. With the appropriate degree of support from the employer, the employee may well be able to resume working and once again become a productive member of staff.

This chapter approaches the subject of attendance management from a practical perspective and aims to provide HR practitioners and line managers with guidance on what can be done to support the rehabilitation of employees who are, or have been, ill and thus absent from work.

Recognising the Problems that Short-Term and Long-Term Absence can Create

5.2

Sickness is one of the most common causes of employee absence from work. Whilst on the one hand an employee cannot realistically be blamed for developing an illness or falling victim to an accident, the employer, on the other hand, needs to manage its business and make sure it is not prejudiced by the persistent or long-term absence of an employee whose skills and output may be vital to the organisation's interests.

Frequent or long-term periods of sickness absence can create a range of problems for the employer, for example:

- the employee's work does not get done, thus creating a backlog and the inevitable associated dissatisfaction amongst colleagues and customers alike;

- the employee's colleagues may have to carry the burden of additional work;

- employees who are persistently expected to cover for another employee who is off sick may be become disillusioned and demotivated (and hence less productive);

- the extra burden of work imposed on the employee's colleagues may cause stress, leading in turn to sickness absence amongst others;

- customers and clients may be dissatisfied at a perceived lack of continuity; and

- the cost of sick pay may become a serious financial burden for the employer.

Employees' Rights and Duties under their Contracts of Employment   5.3

An employee's contract of employment will remain in force during periods of sickness absence unless it is terminated by either the employer or the employee. It follows that it is the terms of the contract that will determine the rights and duties of an employee who is absent from work as a result of sickness, including the right (if any) to receive contractual sick pay (see **5.4** below).

It is helpful to both the employer and the employee if the contract of employment is designed to state clearly what the employee's rights, entitlements and obligations will be in the event that they cannot attend work as a result of sickness. Alternatively, details of employees' entitlements during periods of short and long-term sickness absence can be specified in an employee handbook and a statement made in the employee's written statement of key terms and conditions of employment that the handbook (or the part of the handbook that deals with sickness absence) forms part of their contract. If employees' rights and obligations are not clearly spelled out, this is likely to cause uncertainty for the employee leading perhaps to argument at a later date as to what the employee's entitlements are. Clearly this is in the interests of neither the employer nor the employee.

Broadly, the employer may wish to formulate contractual guidelines to cover:

- notification of sickness absence, both on the first day of absence and at regular intervals thereafter;

- the provision of self-certificates and doctors' certificates;

- eligibility for payment of sick pay over and above the statutory minimum;

- return to work interviews; and

- the employee's duty to agree to be examined by a company nominated doctor at the reasonable request of the employer.

Provided the rules on sickness absence, notification medical certificates and medical examinations form part of employees' contract of employment, the employer will be in a position to enforce their policy and rules fairly and consistently and employees will have a clear picture as what their obligations and entitlements are. Clear contractual guidelines therefore represent the starting point for effective attendance management.

Sickness absence and sick pay   5.4

All employees (including part-timers) are entitled in law to be given a written statement of the key terms and conditions of their employment within eight weeks of starting work. The only exception is where the employee's contract is set up to last for less than one month. Amongst the written information which employers are obliged to provide to employees is the detail of any contractual terms and conditions relating to sickness absence and the provision of sick pay. This relates to the continuation of the employee's wages or salary during periods of sickness absence (usually known as 'contractual sick pay' or 'occupational sick pay'), and not to the entirely separate provision for SSP, payment of which is required by law.

The duty to state in writing what sick pay employees will receive does not, however, place the employer under any legal obligation to pay wages or salary to an employee who is unable to attend work due to sickness, but instead obliges the employer simply to state in writing what, if any, contractual sick pay the employee will receive if they are off work due to sickness or injury. If the employer's policy is not to pay contractual sick pay, then all they need do is state this fact clearly in the employee's written statement of key terms and conditions, or in the contract itself. In this case, only SSP will be payable. Many employers do, however, elect to pay full or part wages or salary to employees for a defined period of time in the event that they are absent from work due to genuine sickness or injury.

Many employers make the payment of contractual sick pay discretionary. Whilst this may seem to offer flexibility to the employer to decide in each individual case whether or not to continue to pay the employee's salary, it also brings with it doubts, potential problems and the possibility of legal challenge. Clearly an employee will feel disgruntled if the employer exercises discretion against them and they find themselves receiving only SSP, especially in circumstances where they may have expected (whether realistically or otherwise) to be paid full salary whilst off sick. Allowing individual line managers to make their own decisions about whether or not to pay an employee who is off sick on any particular occasion is likely to create inconsistency and perceptions of unfairness.

Where an employer nevertheless wishes to operate a discretionary sick pay scheme, they should at the very least:

- specify in employees' contracts (or in an employee handbook which forms part of the contracts) what factors management will take into account when deciding whether or not to pay contractual sick pay;

- state whether payment of sick pay is dependant on any specific factors, for example length of service or performance; and

- ensure that discretion is applied objectively and does not depend on the personal views of any individual line manager.

The employer should ensure that all line managers who have the authority to make decisions on whether or not sick pay should be paid are issued with guidelines on exercising discretion in this area and a clear remit that personal factors (such as personal liking or dislike of the employee) must play no part in any decision.

An alternative approach would be to state in employees' contracts that payment of contractual sick pay for a defined period of time is the norm, but that management reserves the right to elect to withhold sick pay from an employee in circumstances where they consider that there is a sound and objective reason for doing so. Reasons for withholding sick pay could, for example, include situations where:

- the number of days sickness absence, or the number of separate occasions on which the employee has been absent, has exceeded a defined number within a stated period of time;

- the employee is under investigation for a disciplinary offence;

- there are reasonable grounds for the employer to believe that the employee's sickness absence is not genuine (which would in turn give rise to cause for disciplinary action against the employee); or

- the employee has failed to comply with the employer's rules regarding notification of sickness absence or the provision of medical certificates.

Payment of sick pay should never be withheld, however, where the employee's absence has occurred as a result of an injury sustained in the workplace.

Many employers use a defined formula to lay down entitlement to sick pay, often based on a progressive scale to allow those with longer service to qualify for payment for longer periods of time. A common approach is to pay full salary for a fixed period of time, followed by an equivalent period at half pay.

Although there is no legal duty on employers to pay wages or salary to an employee who is unable to attend work as a result of illness or injury, once the employer has recovered and is once again medically fit to work, the employer must at that point reinstate the employee's normal pay (assuming the employee has not resigned or been dismissed in the interim period). In *Beveridge v KLM UK Ltd [2000] IRLR 765*, the EAT ruled that an employer had no right to withhold wages from an employee whose GP had stated she was fit to return to work after a period of sickness absence. The employer had wanted to postpone the employee's return until its own occupational doctor had certified the employee fit to work. Although the employer could have legitimately declined to allow the employee to recommence work, it could not lawfully withhold pay.

Entitlement to benefit under a permanent health insurance scheme 5.5

Many larger employers operate a long-term sickness benefit scheme, sometimes known as a permanent health insurance (PHI) scheme or long-term occupational disability scheme. Such a scheme, normally funded by an external insurance provider, will remove the financial burden from the employer of paying ongoing sick pay to employees who have developed an illness or sustained an injury that is likely to result in long-term absence from work.

Under a typical PHI scheme, employees who are incapacitated and thus unable to work receive a defined level of income, normally expressed as a percentage of pensionable salary (often two-thirds) funded by the insurance company that underwrites the scheme. Typically, PHI will start after a deferment period of six months and will be payable until the employee returns to work, reaches normal retirement age, dies or has their contract of employment terminated. Such a scheme can provide a great deal of comfort and confidence to employees (and their families) that, in the event of long-term incapacity, they are guaranteed to continue to receive an income.

Since it is clearly in the interests of the providers of this type of insurance to limit the length of time that employees are absent from work, many offer help to employers with the rehabilitation of employees who are on long-term sick leave.

Employers should take care, when setting up or reviewing the terms of a PHI scheme, to communicate clearly to their employees what the terms and conditions for receipt of benefit under the scheme will be. In particular, employees' contracts should make it clear whether and in what circumstances the employer may dismiss an employee who is on long-term sick leave and in receipt of benefit. It would, after all, be absurd (and in breach of contract) to promise an employee that they will receive benefit under a PHI scheme if they are off sick long term, and then deny them the promised benefit by dismissing them. There has been a line of court and tribunal decisions upholding the general principle that there will be a breach of contract in circumstances where an employee is dismissed on grounds of sickness absence and the dismissal results in their losing their contractual entitlement to payment under a PHI scheme. Such cases include *Adin v Sedco Forex International Resources Ltd [1997] IRLR 280* and *Villella v MFI Furniture Centres Ltd [1999] IRLR 468.*

In the *Adin* case, the employee had a contractual entitlement to payment of benefit under his employer's short-term (up to twelve months) and long-term (after twelve months) disability schemes. Following a period of short-term absence at the end of which the employee was released from medical care, the employer dismissed him on the grounds that there was no longer a suitable position for him in the company. This meant that, when he fell ill again at a later date, he did not qualify for benefit as he was no longer employed. A claim for breach of contract succeeded as the Court took the view that the employee was entitled, once payment of benefit had begun under the employer's package, to continue to receive it and not to have his continuing benefits taken away from him at the employer's discretion through being dismissed.

In the *Villella* case, the employee's contract stated that he would receive PHI benefit until he was fit to return to work, reached age 65, or died, whichever occurred first. Nothing was said in the employee's contract about continuation of benefit being dependant on the employee remaining in employment. When the employee became incapacitated, he began receiving benefit under the scheme. After a few months, however, the insurance provider notified the employer that, based on medical evidence, they had decided to stop paying out the benefit. For a short time thereafter, the employer continued to fund the employee's benefit themselves, but soon afterwards dismissed him, thus bringing all payments to an end. The High Court noted that the agreement between the employer and the insurance provider contained a restriction that benefit would not be payable to someone who was no longer an employee. Because the employee's contract contained no parallel restriction, however, the Court ruled that he was entitled to continue to receive benefit from the employer under the terms of his contract until his return to work, attainment of age 65 or death. This meant that the employer was left with the financial burden of paying the benefit.

In contrast, in *Hill v General Accident Fire & Life Assurance Corporation plc [1998] IRLR 641*, the Court held that the dismissal of an absent employee by reason of redundancy was not in breach of the employee's contract, even though the dismissal had the effect of terminating the employee's entitlement to benefit under the employer's long-term sick pay scheme. The difference between this case and the two cases described above is that the employee's dismissal was on account of redundancy whilst in the other two cases the reason for dismissal was associated with sickness absence.

Employers should therefore not be tempted to dismiss an employee who has a contractual entitlement to PHI benefit if the dismissal would deprive them of the continuation of the benefit. The circumstances in which an employee in receipt of long-term sickness benefit can be lawfully dismissed (if the dismissal would deprive them of contractual sick pay or PHI benefit) are in effect limited to occasions when dismissal is by reason of redundancy or gross misconduct.

As a result of case law, employers should, when setting up or reviewing their benefits packages for employees on long-term sickness absence:

- scrutinise the terms of the agreement with the insurance provider, in particular to establish whether there are any restrictions regarding payment to employees whose employment is terminated;

- establish clearly what the insurance provider's criteria for payment of benefit are (for example whether it is necessary for the employee to be totally incapacitated or just unable to perform their own job), and communicate these clearly to employees;

- ensure that the terms of employees' contracts properly reflect the terms and benefits agreed with the insurance provider; and

- ensure that the terms of employees' contracts clearly state any restrictions on benefit being paid and the full range of circumstances under which benefit may be stopped.

One way of handling the matter is simply to incorporate the main terms of the insurance provider's policy agreement into employees' contracts of employment.

Notification of sickness absence 5.6

It is advisable for employers to formulate and implement clear rules for notification of sickness absence. Such rules may include requirements for employees:

- to notify their line manager by telephone within a defined time-frame on the first day of their absence that they will be unable to attend work, and the reason why;

- (similarly) to notify their line manager as early as possible where the employee knows in advance that they will be absent from work at a particular time (for example if they are going into hospital for an operation);

- to maintain contact every three to five days in order to inform their line manager of their progress and when they expect to be able to return to work; or

- (where the employee is off sick long-term) to provide regular medical certificates at set intervals.

It is advisable for employers to require employers to make contact with a defined person when first notifying sickness absence, preferably their line manager, rather than simply expecting them to 'phone in'.

Duty to agree to attend a medical examination at the employer's request 5.7

When an employee is absent from work due to sickness, it may be important for the employer to obtain medical evidence in the form of regular doctors' certificates confirming that the employee is unable to attend work. Over and above this, it may be useful or even necessary to seek medical advice in the form of a report in order to establish the facts relating to an employee's incapacity for work. There are a number of circumstances in which this will be important, for example in order to:

- ascertain the likelihood of the employee recovering sufficiently to return to work in the foreseeable future;

- establish the likely length of time the employee will be absent, so that the employer can make alternative arrangements to cover the employee's work (for example by hiring a temporary worker from an employment agency);

- ascertain the likelihood of the employee's illness worsening, or recurring at a later date after an initial recovery;

- learn whether the employee's illness or injury may cause them a permanent impairment that could prevent them resuming their normal job duties;

- consider whether it would be advisable to discuss with the employee the possibility of a transfer to different work or part-time work; and

- establish whether the employee is genuinely fit to resume working, especially if the job duties are physically or mentally demanding.

If the employer wishes to use the services of an occupational doctor, it is advisable to include within the terms of employees' contracts of employment a clear statement that obliges employees to consent to attend a medical examination with an occupational doctor if reasonably asked to do so by the employer. Putting pressure on an employee to agree to a doctor's examination without contractual authority would constitute a breach of contract and possibly also a breach of the employee's right to privacy under Article 8 of the *Human Rights Act 2000*. This in turn could give rise to a claim for constructive dismissal (subject to the employee having a minimum of one year's service) if the employee chose to resign on account of the employer's actions.

Provided there is a contractual rule that obliges employees to agree to be examined by an employer-nominated doctor at the request of the employer, any refusal on the part of the employee to consent to attend a medical when reasonably asked to do so would constitute a breach of contract on the part of the employee. This would allow the employer to take disciplinary action against the employee, provided the request itself was reasonable and the employee's refusal without good reason. It should of course, be clearly stated in the employer's sickness absence policy and in employees' contracts that a breach of the rules in this respect will be regarded as a disciplinary offence.

Flexibility clauses   5.8

It may happen that an employee who has been absent from work due to long-term sickness is no longer capable of performing their job, even though they may have recovered sufficiently to return to work. This is particularly likely in the case of physically strenuous or mentally demanding jobs or jobs involving a lot of travel. In this case, the employer will want to have the flexibility to move the employee to a different, possibly less demanding job.

It is helpful to employers if they design employees' contracts to include flexibility clauses with regard to job duties, work location and hours of work. If the employee has at the outset of employment agreed (by signing their contract) that the employer may move them to different job duties, a different job, different hours of work or shift patterns or a different location, then the employer will have the authority to redeploy the employee on their return to work from sickness absence if it proves necessary or desirable to do so.

Even though such changes may have been expressly agreed in advance between the employer and the employee, the employer should nevertheless discuss any proposed changes with the employee and seek to secure their consent to any specific changes at the relevant time. There would be little point in forcing an unwelcome move on an employee even where contractual authority existed to do so, as this would be unlikely to achieve a positive outcome.

Example flexibility clauses   5.9

1	The Employer reserves the right to ask you to undertake different or additional job duties from those outlined in your job description, depending on the needs of the business. You are required by your contract to agree to perform such different job duties provided it is reasonably within your skills and capabilities to do so.
2	The Employer reserves the right to require you to transfer to a different job upon reasonable request, depending on the needs of the business and on your performance and capabilities. It is a condition of your contract that you agree to any such transfer upon reasonable request.
3	The Employer reserves the right to require you to change your hours of work [shift pattern], whether temporarily or permanently, according to the needs of the business. This provision includes an increase or decrease to the number of hours you are required to work. It is a condition of your contract of employment that you agree to any request of this nature that is reasonably made.
4	The Employer reserves the right to require you to transfer from your normal place of work to any other place of work within [ ] miles of [ ]/within reasonable commuting distance of your home/within the United Kingdom, whether temporarily or permanently. You are required by your contract to agree to any such move upon reasonable request. The Employer will give you not less than [ ] weeks' notice of any such requirement.

Managing Intermittent Short-Term Absences   5.10

All line managers responsible for staff should, as part of their management responsibilities, be expected to manage and control short-term absence and attendance, and ensure their employer's policies on absence and attendance are translated into practice.

Even though short-term absences from work may be for entirely genuine reasons, they may cause serious disruption for the employer who may not be able to rely on the employee to perform their work with any regularity. The employer may legitimately take action to deal with the problem of frequent absences on the part of a particular employee and there are a number of practical steps that can be taken, namely:

- institute a proper procedure each time an employee phones in sick;
- conduct routine 'return-to-work interviews';
- ensure employees always complete self-certification forms for short periods of sickness absence;
- explore the cause(s) of persistent short-term absences, including a check on whether there might be a pattern to the absences;

- seek medical advice, if appropriate, to determine whether there is any underlying medical cause for the employee's frequent absences;

- set targets and time limits for improvement in attendance;

- warn the employee of the likely consequences of continuing unsatisfactory attendance;

- keep confidential records of all absences, discussions and medical certificates; and

- set trigger points for formal action.

These issues are explored further below.

Procedure when an employee phones in sick   5.11

Many employers have no formal procedure as regards what should take place when an employee phones in to alert their employer that they are sick. Messages may not be passed on to the right person and often HR department are not reliably advised of the requirement to institute SSP.

In order to avoid these possible problems, ensure consistency and manage attendance effectively, employers should put in place a procedure which states what should happen when an employee first notifies the employer of sickness absence. The policy, which should cover all absences including those likely to last only half a day, should cover:

- the requirement for the employee to phone a designated person, not just anyone;

- the requirement for the person taking the telephone call to create a record of the call; and

- the requirement for the person taking the call to ask the employee pre-set questions, in particular the precise reason for the absence and how long the employee thinks they will be absent, and record the employee's answers.

A convenient way to handle this first step in the attendance management process is to devise a telephone questionnaire to capture what is said. Sections on the questionnaire could include:

- who phoned in (ie was it the employee personally or a friend or relative);

- who took the call;

- the time and date of the call;

- the stated reason for the employee's inability to attend work (for example whether the absence is due to illness, injury, personal or family reasons or some other reason, and if due to illness or injury, the nature of the illness or injury, eg stomach upset, flu, etc);

- whether the absence is in any way related to factors at work;

- the employee's opinion on how long they expect to be absent;

- what, if any, drugs or other treatment the employee is taking or receiving;

- whether the employee has seen, or intends to see, their GP;

- the line manager's comments, if any, on the employee's call;

- a call-back log, ie a note of whether the line manager has called the employee back, the reason for the call-back and the outcome; and

- the line manager's signature.

The questionnaire can also be used as the trigger for the employer to instigate the appropriate procedure for payment of SSP.

Conducting return-to-work interviews   5.12

Each time an employee has been absent from work (irrespective of the duration of the absence), the line manager should make a point of speaking to the employee on their return. This should be done in a positive, supportive and factual way. This approach will alert the employee to the fact the manager is monitoring the situation and will potentially deter casual absences. Such an 'interview' should be informal, so there would be no legal right for the employee to be accompanied (although it is open to the employer to agree to allow someone else to be present if the employee makes a reasonable request to that effect). It should of course be made clear to the employee that the interview is a review meeting and not a disciplinary interview. Although the interview will be informal, it should nevertheless be structured and recorded and should not just be a casual 'corridor chat'. It should also be private and confidential. The key points for discussion will include:

- the reason for the employee's absence;

- the nature of the illness or injury, and whether it was a 'one-off', for example a stomach upset, or whether it was due to a condition that is likely to recur (the employee should not, however, be expected to disclose details of any medical condition);

- whether the employee consulted their doctor, or attended hospital;

- whether the employee is now fully, or only partially, recovered;

- whether the employer can do anything to help or support the employee;

- whether there is any underlying problem in the workplace which is causing or contributing to the employee's absences; and

- a review of the employee's overall absence record to establish whether the trigger point under the employer's attendance procedure has been reached (in which case a formal interview may need to be set up).

The manager conducting this type of interview should be supportive towards the employee and, where appropriate, have as their main aim the identification of ways in which they could assist the employee to improve their attendance in the future.

The HR department may wish to consider providing training to line managers in the skills required for such interviews, so that line managers are able to:

- carry out return-to-work interviews fairly and objectively;

- frame questions so that they elicit meaningful answers;

- probe problem areas where appropriate without sounding critical or intrusive;

- spot any signs of stress in the employee;

- discern when it is appropriate to adopt a sympathetic approach and when a more firm stance may be appropriate; and

- understand the key principles of the *Disability Discrimination Act 1995* and (as it relates to health and attendance records) the *Data Protection Act 1998*.

Self-certification   5.13

During the course of the return to work interview, the line manager should require the employee to complete a self-certification form for all periods of short-term absence (usually up to one calendar week). The employee should be asked to complete and sign the form in front of the manager, who should then counter-sign the form for the record.

It is a good idea to design self-certification forms so that they require the employee to write the reason for their sickness absence and the dates of their absence on to the form, rather than just tick a series of boxes. This makes the process of self-certification a more active process.

It is also advisable to ensure that employees' contracts state clearly that payment of sick pay is conditional upon the completion of a self-certification form on return to work (and on the provision of doctors' certificates in the case of longer periods of absence).

Exploring the cause(s) of the employee's absences   5.14

Line managers should take steps to explore the cause or causes of persistent short-term absences, including looking to see whether a pattern exists. For example, there may be a pattern of frequent Monday absences, or a pattern that indicates that the employee goes off sick each time they are under stress or facing an imminent deadline.

If a pattern is identified, the manager's observations should be put to the employee directly so that the employee has the opportunity to provide an explanation. Managers should remain open-minded and not jump to any hasty conclusions.

The line manager's objective in holding such discussions with an employee should be try to establish, through investigation and discussion, the underlying reasons(s) for the employee's frequent absences. Until the underlying cause is identified, an appropriate and effective remedy will be hard to identify.

The manager should consider (and ask the employee) whether the absences are due in part to personal or family problems. If this is the case, a reasonable degree of tolerance and sympathy should be shown towards the employee as the problems may be unavoidable. The manager should be supportive, whilst at the same time explaining clearly to the employee that continuing frequent absences from work are unacceptable.

Another important check will be to establish whether the employee's absences are in any way work related. If the absence problem is work related, prompt steps should be taken to remove or reduce the factor that is causing the problem. There is no point in telling the employee that they must simply learn to cope, or that nothing can be done, because the absence problem will continue and the factor that is causing it may escalate and develop into a major crisis.

It will be essential to conduct the process of investigation with an open mind and recognise that the cause of the employee's persistent absences may be outside their control. Understanding the root cause of the absence problem is important because, until the source of the problem is correctly diagnosed, an appropriate course of action to remedy the problem will not be able to be identified. Some examples of employer actions which would definitely not remedy the root cause of an absence problem could be:

- applying disciplinary procedures to an employee whose absences are as a result of their need to care for an elderly relative whose health has recently deteriorated;

- telling an employee to 'buck-up and be less sensitive' in circumstances where absences have been caused by problem relationships at work, or bullying;

- responding to an employee's absences caused by stress at work by placing even more pressure on them; or

- giving an employee who has a drug or alcohol addiction a warning, without first offering the opportunity for rehabilitation, counselling or time off to undergo appropriate treatment.

If, on the other hand, the employee's absences are within their control, for example if absence is due to tiredness and the tiredness is in turn due to the fact the employee has a second job, then the matter should be fully discussed with the employee with a view to achieving specific targeted improvements (see **5.16** below).

Seeking medical advice   5.15

It may be helpful to obtain professional medical advice in relation to an employee who has had frequent short-term absences from work in order to ascertain or confirm whether there is any underlying medical condition causing the absences. The result of a doctor's report may be that the employee is genuinely suffering from an illness or other condition that flares up occasionally rendering the employee incapable of attending work. On the other hand, medical evidence may suggest that the employee is fit and healthy and it may therefore be deduced that the employee is either:

- more prone than most to various ailments such as flu, colds etc which are causing genuine absences from work; or

- taking time off work for reasons other than ill health, which the employer should discuss with the employee at a private interview in order to seek out the truth behind the employee's frequent absences – reasons may include workplace stress, problem relationships at work, bullying or harassment, drug or alcohol abuse, personal or family problems or even poor attitude.

Details about obtaining medical advice are contained below at **5.30**.

Setting targets and time limits for improvement   5.16

During discussions with the employee, the line manager should seek to agree with the employee reasonable targets and time limits for improvement in attendance and ensure the employee is committed to achieving these. When the time limit is up, the manager should of course review the situation again in conjunction with the employee.

Giving warnings for unsatisfactory attendance   5.17

Irrespective of the reasons for an employee's frequent absences from work, if the number of absences has become excessive or has reached the stage where the absences are causing serious difficulties or disruption, the employee should be informed of this fact and warned that if a satisfactory level of attendance is not achieved within a stated timescale, then formal warnings may follow, leading potentially to dismissal eventually.

Where absences are for genuine reasons, such warnings are not technically disciplinary warnings (unless there is evidence that some or all of the absences are without any valid reason), but may be termed 'capability warnings' or 'attendance warnings'. The purpose of such a warning is to inform the employee on a formal basis that, unless a satisfactory and sustained improvement in attendance is achieved, the problem may lead eventually to the termination of the employee's employment. This situation may arise even in cases where the employee's absences are indisputably genuine and even where the employee's manager may feel a considerable degree of sympathy and support for the employee. Such sympathy and support, although wholly appropriate in cases of genuine ill health, does not remove the need for the employee's work to be done on a regular and reliable basis. As part of any attendance warning, the employee should be informed clearly and specifically what improvement in attendance is required, and a time limit should be agreed for reappraising the situation.

Keeping records   5.18

Employers should keep confidential records of all absences, discussions and medical certificates and make sure the record clearly identifies the reasons for the employee's various absences. Normally these records should be held by the HR department, but irrespective of where they are held they must be treated as confidential and with due regard to the provisions of the *Data Protection Act 1998 (DPA 1988)*. The *DPA 1988* classifies health information as 'sensitive data' which can be collected and processed only subject to very strict conditions.

Maintaining comprehensive records of an employee's sickness absences will be an essential foundation for tackling the problem with the employee once the absences have exceeded a defined number (see 'adhering to trigger points' at **5.19** below). It will be necessary for the employer, before instituting any action against an employee who has had frequent short-term absences from work, to check the employee's absence record carefully. This will be in order to gain an accurate picture of the number of days absence the employee has had, the number of separate occasions they have been absent and whether their record is tangibly worse than that of other employees in the organisation.

Adhering to trigger points   5.19

It is helpful for employers to define trigger points beyond which the employee will become subject to the employer's formal absence and attendance management policy, as opposed to the informal procedures described above. The trigger points will be based on two key factors, namely:

- the number of absences the employee has had within a defined time period (usually a year); and

- the length of each absence.

A typical trigger point might be three separate absences (irrespective of their length) or absences totalling twelve or 15 days in any twelve-month period. Another type of trigger could be when the employee's manager has reasonable grounds to believe that a pattern of absence has developed and wishes to investigate that pattern under the employer's formal procedure. An example could be where the employee has had three Monday absences in a six-month period.

When a trigger point is reached, the implication will be that the employee's level of attendance is unsatisfactory and measures must be sought to achieve an improvement.

Persistent short-term absence   5.20

Many employers are reluctant to apply robust management techniques in the case of an employee who is persistently absent, even where it is suspected that the employee is malingering. The application of the processes recommended earlier in this section, such as using telephone questionnaires when an employee first phones in sick and always conducting routine return-to-work interviews will help in the management of persistent absentees, as these processes may deter casual absence and at the very least alert the employee to the fact they are being monitored. They will also alert management to any underlying problem which they can then address, for example if absences are found to be work related.

Once a trigger point (see **5.19** above) has been reached, management should implement a formal absence and attendance procedure. The first step in the procedure will be to set up an interview, at which the employee should be allowed (if they wish) to be accompanied by a colleague or trade union official of their choice. The purposes of the interview will be to:

* inform the employee that their level of absence has become unacceptable;

* explore (once again) the cause or causes of the absences;

* listen with an open mind to any representations that the employee may wish to make;

* warn the employee that if their attendance level does not improve to an agreed level within an agreed time-frame, they will face further action under the employer's absence and attendance procedure; and

* reach a conclusion as to what action is to be taken.

Future action is likely to be one of the following:

* continued monitoring of the employee's attendance – in conjunction targets and time-scales for improvement;

* referral to an occupational health specialist to explore the possibility of the absences being due to an underlying medical cause; or

* transfer to the employer's disciplinary procedure and a stage one disciplinary warning.

If the employee's attendance subsequently does not improve to the level specified at the interview, the employee will move through the absence and attendance procedure in defined stages, possibly all the way to dismissal. If, however, an underlying health problem is established, the employer will be in a position to ensure that the employee receives the appropriate support, including any contractual sick pay or PHI benefit to which they may be entitled. Much will depend on the outcome of the absence and attendance procedure.

Sickness Absence During Pregnancy 5.21

Special care should be exercised in the case of sickness absence during the time when an employee is pregnant. The employer should make absolutely certain that no employee is penalised or disadvantaged in any way on account of being unwell and unable to attend work, irrespective of whether the employee's illness is pregnancy-related.

There is a long line of case law in Britain and at European level which has clearly established that any unfavourable treatment of a female employee on any grounds related (whether directly or indirectly) to pregnancy will be regarded as unlawful direct sex discrimination. For example, in *Brown v Rentokil [1998] IRLR 445*, an employee who became pregnant and consequently suffered ill health and was absent for six months was dismissed in accordance with her employer's contractual sickness absence policy. The policy decreed that any employee who exceeded 26 weeks continuous sickness absence would be automatically dismissed. Despite the policy, the employee succeeded in her claim for sex discrimination at the European Court of Justice. The dismissal was for reasons linked to pregnancy, and since pregnancy is a gender-specific condition (ie it can only happen to women), the dismissal was for reasons linked to gender. The Court expressed the view that, although there was no inherent unfairness in the policy itself, the employer should have disapplied it in the case of Ms Brown.

The *Brown* case concerned a dismissal for reasons connected with pregnancy-related sickness absence. Similarly, however, if an employee is treated unfavourably as regards entitlement to sick pay or other benefits on account of the fact that her absence occurs during pregnancy, this would also constitute unlawful sex discrimination.

It follows that an employee who is absent from work whilst pregnant should be treated in the same manner as any other employee who is unable to come to work on account of illness. If the employer operates a discretionary sick pay policy, it would be advisable to exercise discretion in the employee's favour, ie to pay her the maximum amount of sick pay available under the policy. SSP will also be payable in the usual way.

There are, however, special rules that apply during the final four weeks of an employee's pregnancy. If, during this period, the employee is still working and becomes unable to attend work for a pregnancy-related reason, the employer is entitled to 'trigger' (ie enforce) the start of the employee's maternity leave at that point in time. This would mean that normal salary, contractual sick pay and SSP would cease and (in most cases) the employee would become eligible to receive statutory maternity pay.

it is important to note that, if an employee is absent from work due to sickness that is unrelated to pregnancy during the four weeks immediately before the

125

week her baby is expected, the triggering provisions described above will not be engaged. The absence must be pregnancy-related for this to be the case.

Managing Long-Term Sickness Absence 5.22

Despite the fact that long-term sickness absence is much rarer than one-day absences, it accounts for more than 30 per cent of all time lost due to sickness absence in the UK. The effective management of long-term sickness absence is therefore an important organisational responsibility. 'Long-term' absence will usually be defined as a period of sickness lasting four weeks or more (although different organisations may, of course, opt for a different definition).

A case management approach 5.23

An employer that adopts a 'case management' approach towards an employee on long-term sickness absence will increase the chances of the employee returning to work and remaining in employment, and reduce overall sickness absence costs into the bargain. A case management approach will bring all the relevant people in the organisation together to discuss the individual employee's case at regular intervals, for example quarterly. The relevant people will include:

- the employee or their representative;

- the employee's line manager;

- the HR manager;

- a representative from occupational health;

- (possibly) a health and safety officer; and

- (possibly) the employee's GP or specialist.

Case management involves:

- being proactive in relation to the employee's absence and rehabilitation;

- regular communication between line management, HR management and occupational health;

- early intervention through referral to occupational health (and subsequent re-assessment at pre-defined intervals); and

- a focus on rehabilitating the employee back into the workplace as soon as possible, whether in their own job or another job.

In order to achieve the above, the employer should devise and implement a clear case management plan which should be agreed with the employee at an early stage.

At each case management review meeting, the following issues should be addressed:

- the total length of time the employee has been absent from work;

- the effects of the employee's absence on the work of the department, and the extent of any difficulties being experienced;

- the estimated further length of time the employee is likely to be absent, and the potential impact of further absence;

- whether or not the employee is likely to be capable of performing their own job, or an alternative job (for example a less demanding job) in the foreseeable future;

- the possibility of transferring the employee to alternative work, or part-time work, if that would help them ease back into working;

- whether the employee's condition is likely to fall within the definition of 'disability' contained in the *Disability Discrimination Act 1995*, and if so what reasonable adjustments the employer could make to facilitate the employee's return to work; and

- whether the employee is still receiving statutory or occupational sick pay, and for how much longer entitlement will continue.

It will be very important for the employer to consult the employee and it may be preferable to invite the employee to at least some of the case review meetings (if they are well enough to attend).

Medical information and advice will obviously represent a key element of the employee's case management. As part of case management, the employer should adopt a policy of requiring employees who are absent from work long term to undergo regular (for example quarterly or six-monthly) medical examinations with an occupational doctor (see below at **5.30**).

Maintaining contact 5.24

Whenever an employee is off sick for a lengthy period of time, someone from the organisation, for example the employee's line manager or a representative from HR, should maintain regular contact with them. Arguably, it is the line manager's responsibility to fulfil this role. This contact may be vital for the employee to maintain a link with their employment and avoid isolation, and the contact will have the added advantage of letting the employee know that the employer genuinely cares about their well-being.

Some managers may feel uneasy about the prospect of contacting an employee at home, fearing that the employee may view the contact as an intrusion, or even as harassment, or that it might put undue pressure on the employee and make matters worse. Whilst these fears are understandable, they may well be unfounded. In most cases, it is likely that the employee who is ill and off work will feel isolated and miss the regular contact with workmates. Regular visits or phone calls from the workplace may be the person's only link to their 'normal' life and may be very welcome, so long as no pressure of any kind is put on the employee. Lack of contact, on the other hand, may make the employee feel unwanted or undervalued.

It should be agreed at an early stage of the employee's absence how often contact will be made, by whom it will be made and how it will be made, for example by telephone or by someone visiting the employee at home. Alternatively, the employee may be fit enough to visit the workplace even though they are not fit enough to work. If in doubt, the best way forward is to ask the employee whether (for example) they would like someone from the organisation to visit them at home (or in hospital) or whether they would prefer only telephone contact. At the same time, it will be very important to reassure the employee that the contact is intended to be supportive. The employee's views on how contact should be made should, however, be respected.

Contact with the employee should always be co-ordinated, so that the employee does not receive a number of contacts from different people at random intervals.

The main aims of regular contact will be to:

- understand the cause(s) of the employee's absence;
- enable the employer to keep up to date with the employee's well-being and progress;
- reassure the employee about practical issues, for example that their job is safe;
- demonstrate to the employee that they are not forgotten;
- show the employee that the employer is genuinely interested and concerned about their health and well-being;
- keep the employee informed and involved in general company or departmental matters; and
- discuss the employee's progress and (where appropriate) their return to work.

Naturally, the person who is responsible for maintaining contact with the employee should adopt a supportive approach and should take care not to put undue pressure on the employee, or make them feel guilty about being absent.

Another action that the employer may wish to take is to invite the employee (if they are well enough) to workplace social events. Just because an employee is signed off work does not necessarily mean that it is unfeasible or inappropriate for them to go out socially. On the contrary, an employee who is absent from work on account of an injury or a stress-related illness may benefit from the occasional 'night out'. Including the employee in such events can have the added advantage of demonstrating that the employer still views the person as one of the team.

Managing the return to work of an employee who has been absent long term   5.25

It is important for employers to take responsibility for helping employees return to work after a prolonged absence. Thus when an employee who has been absent from work for a lengthy period of time is certified fit to resume working, the employer may wish to take certain procedural steps, for example:

- arrange for the employee to be examined by an occupational doctor to make sure they are genuinely fit to resume full-time working in their normal job;

- consider specific advice from occupational health, for example whether the employee should be exempted initially from any work that is physically demanding or mentally stressful (taking into account any factors that contributed to the employee's absence in the first place);

- review whether there are likely to be any health and safety implications upon the employee's return to work;

- arrange a social visit for the employee prior to their resuming work, so that the employee can meet with their colleagues and their line manager;

- if the employee is not fit to work full-time, or to resume working in their own job, consider alternative working patterns or job duties (see **5.28** below);

- set up a meeting with the employee upon their return (or just prior to their return) to discuss their capabilities and to review whether any special arrangements need to be made to support them initially; and

- agree with the employee what support will be available during the first weeks or months after their return, and how their progress will be monitored.

The option of a phased return to work   5.26

In many cases, a phased return to work will help the employee make the transition from being at home full-time to working full-time. A phased return could involve:

- part-time working for a time, for example starting with two days a week, then progressing to three, then eventually to five;

- working shorter days, for example four or five hours a day rather than eight initially;

- working at home two or three days a week to start with; or

- a combination of any of the above.

All possible options should be discussed fully with the employee prior to their return to work, with a view to reaching agreement on the initial working pattern and number of hours of work expected of the employee and when this will fall to be reviewed. A target timescale for the resumption of full-time working should also be agreed, with the option to review and revise this timescale if necessary.

Workplace or job adjustments 5.27

If the employee's condition amounts to a disability as defined in the *Disability Discrimination Act 1995* (see **CHAPTER 4** for details of the Act), the employer will be under a duty to make reasonable adjustments to working arrangements, working practices and the physical environment (as appropriate) to accommodate the employee's particular needs. A failure to carry out this duty will amount to unlawful disability discrimination.

The best way to approach the issue of reasonable adjustments is to hold discussions with the employee to seek their views on what changes to working practices or working conditions would help them to return to work or perform their job more effectively. In most cases, the employee will have more knowledge than anyone else as to what type of support would be relevant and helpful. The employer should therefore fully consider any adjustments suggested by the employee that might facilitate a return to work.

The employer should, however, not overlook the fact that the duty to address the issue of whether reasonable adjustments can be made is the statutory responsibility of the employer, and not the employee. They should therefore be prepared to take the initiative and endeavour to identify suitable steps that can be taken to support the employee.

Some examples of workplace or job adjustments that might help an employee return to work and/or work more effectively are as follows:

- agree a phased return to work (see **5.26** above);

- alter working hours or shift patterns, whether temporarily or permanently;

- permit more frequent or longer rest breaks for a period of time, for example if the employee's condition means that they tire easily or if they need to take medication at regular intervals;

- permit the employee to take reasonable time off work to attend medical appointments, rehabilitation, counselling or therapy;

- allow the employee to work wholly or partly at home for a while;

- exempt the employee from any aspects of their job that are particularly demanding, whether physically or mentally;

- review whether the employee has any specific training needs as a result of their condition, and take steps to fulfil these needs;

- discuss whether any special equipment is needed for the employee in order for them to perform their job effectively;

- review the employee's physical environment to assess whether any changes would help the employee to work more effectively; or

- be willing to make exceptions to company policies and procedures, for example by exempting a disabled employee from the strict rules of an attendance procedure or excluding disability-related absences from any calculations of overall attendance when considering warnings or dismissal.

In *London Borough of Hillingdon v Morgan EAT 1493/98*, the employer was judged to have failed in their duty to make reasonable adjustments when they refused to allow an office-based employee who had been absent from work for eight months with ME to work part-time from home for a temporary period to help her to ease back into full-time employment. The EAT ruled that there was no proper reason why the employee's request (which was on the recommendation of her doctor) could not have been accommodated.

In the case of *Fu v London Borough of Camden [2001] IRLR 186*, the EAT held that an employer must address its mind to what reasonable adjustments can be made for a disabled employee to return to work from a long-term absence before taking a decision to dismiss the employee. Ultimately, the employer should be prepared to do everything they reasonably can to retain the employee in employment.

Although an employer is not obliged to make reasonable adjustments in circumstances where they do not know, and cannot reasonably be expected to know, that the employee is disabled, the Code of Practice for the elimination of discrimination in the field of employment against disabled persons recommends that 'an employer must ... do all he could reasonably be expected to do to find out whether this is the case.' Thus where an employee has been absent from work for a lengthy period of time, the employer could reasonably be expected to realise that the employee may have a condition that amounts to a disability. It follows that the employer should make reasonable enquiries of the employee and of at least one medical adviser as to whether the employee might be disabled (from a legal perspective) and what adjustments would help the employee return to work.

Considering the option of transfer to another job
5.28

In some cases, an employee may be fit to work in a general sense, but not fit enough to carry out their normal job duties. This may be because the job in which they are employed is particularly demanding in terms of physical effort, high volume of work, time-pressures, extensive travel, or rotating shifts or the likelihood that the employee's job could cause an unacceptable level of stress.

In these circumstances, the employer should, together with the employee, review the possibility of transferring the employee to alternative work, or part-time work, if that would help the employee ease back into normal working. The transfer could be either on a temporary or permanent basis, the latter being appropriate if medical evidence suggested that the employee was unlikely in the foreseeable future to be fit enough to fulfil the duties of their own job.

Whenever a change in job duties or a transfer to another job is an option, the possibilities should be discussed directly with the employee. Agreement is essential, as without it a move to a different job, different shift pattern or different duties could constitute a breach of contract.

Supporting the employee on return to work   5.29

There are a number of actions that an employer can, and should, take when an employee returns to work after a lengthy period of absence. It will be important to remember that the employee may feel anxious about returning to work and worry about how they will be treated by their colleagues and by management. Positive steps should be taken to welcome the employee back, make them 'feel at home' and facilitate their re-integration into the workplace. Such steps should include the following:

- make sure the employee knows that their return to work is welcomed and that management are supportive towards their re-integration into the workplace;

- ensure the employee is not 'thrown into the deep end' by exposing them to an enormous in-tray and hundreds of emails on their first day;

- provide the employee with a 'mini-induction' to help them reintegrate into the organisation and to update them on company or departmental activities during the period of their absence;

- if the reason for the employee's absence is 'sensitive' (for example if they have had a mental illness), agree with the employee what information will be provided (if any) to colleagues, and by whom;

- nominate someone to be the employee's 'buddy' or 'mentor' during the first two to three months after their return, ie someone (ideally from another department) who will monitor the employee's well-being and progress, deal with any difficulties the employee may be experiencing and ensure they are coping with their workload and day-to-day pressures;

- give the employee meaningful work to do as soon as possible, and preferably tasks that can be completed in a short period of time (for example a day) as this will enable the employee quickly to feel useful;

- set realistic and achievable goals to enable the employee to gain a sense of achievement, and once the goals are achieved, give positive feedback;

- monitor the employee's work-load initially to ensure they do not take on too much and that too much pressure is not placed on them;

- talk to the employee informally on a regular basis to discuss progress and resolve any problems they may have encountered.

Another point to address is whether the employee will still be taking medication for a period of time after their return to work and whether this medication is likely to have any side effects. An occupational doctor should be asked to give advice on this and management should be aware of, and tolerant of, any possible side effects of the medication on the employee, for example tiredness or poor concentration. The continuation of medication may, in any event, be only temporary.

Referring Employees for a Medical Examination or Report   5.30

When an employee is absent from work due to sickness, whether on an intermittent basis or for a single lengthy period of time, it will be important for the employer to obtain medical advice in order to establish the facts relating to the employee's incapacity for work. Arguably, one of the keys to tackling long-term sickness absence lies in understanding its causes and whether there are any patterns of absence that the employer can address.

Medical advice will be necessary in order to:

• understand the nature of the problem;

• establish the employee's condition, its effects and their fitness to work;

• ascertain the likely length of time the employee will be absent, so that the employer can make alternative arrangements to cover the employee's work;

• learn whether the employee's illness or injury may cause them a permanent impairment that could prevent them resuming their normal job duties;

• determine whether the employee might, if unfit to perform their own job, be capable of performing a different job, for example lighter duties or part-time work;

• establish whether the employee is genuinely fit to resume working, especially if the job duties are physically or mentally demanding;

• consider whether it would be advisable to review the possibility of a transfer to a different job, and if so what type of job; and

• ascertain the likelihood of the employee's illness recurring or worsening either in the short or long-term future.

If, ultimately, the medical prognosis is that the employee is unlikely for some long time to recover sufficiently to return to work, the employer may contemplate offering the employee early retirement (if they are eligible under an occupational scheme) or terminating their employment (see **5.35** below). It will be important to bear in mind, however, that if the employee is dismissed without the input of professional medical advice, the dismissal is likely to be unfair in law. This is because a tribunal would be likely to take the view that the employer had acted unreasonably in not taking available medical evidence into account before taking the decision to dismiss the employee (see **5.35** below).

Medical advice may be sought either from the employee's GP or specialist (with the employee's consent) or from an occupational doctor nominated by the employer. Each has its own advantages (see **5.31–5.33** below). Often the best course of action is to seek to obtain medical information from more than one source and this approach would be particularly recommended if dismissal or ill health retirement was being contemplated.

Irrespective of the source from which medical advice is sought, the employer should provide sufficient meaningful information to the doctor for them to make a reasoned judgement on the employee's condition and fitness to work. Specific questions should be asked of the doctor in order that the employer can obtain specific advice on the employee's fitness to work in their particular environment.

To the employee's GP   5.31

The employee's GP will in all likelihood have fuller knowledge of the employee's medical history and general state of health than an occupational doctor. On the other hand, they will probably have considerably less knowledge of the employee's specific job, its demands or the particular working environment.

Where the employer wishes to obtain a medical report from the employee's GP, they must pay heed to the provisions of the *Access to Medical Reports Act 1988 (AMRA 1988)*. This Act gives employees the right (amongst other rights) to decline or refuse to give consent for their employer to request a medical report from their GP or specialist. The employee is not obliged to give any reason for such a refusal, and must not be penalised in any way for refusing. Without written consent from the employee, the employer will be unable to obtain a report from the GP. Many employees may, however, be happy to agree to this course of action. The employer can start the process by writing to the employee requesting their written consent and informing them of their rights under the Act.

CHAPTER 4 provides further details of the provisions of *AMRA 1988*.

To the employee's specialist   5.32

A specialist will be better placed than either the GP or the occupational doctor to provide detailed advice on the employee's particular condition and how it is likely to affect their general capabilities and day-to-day activities. The *Access to Medical Reports Act 1988* applies equally to reports sought from the employee's specialist or consultant.

To an occupational doctor   5.33

An occupational doctor will normally have a better understanding than either the GP or the specialist of the employee's working conditions, the demands that their job places upon them and the issue of rehabilitation into the workplace. On the other hand, a company doctor may not have the same level of insight into the employee's medical history or general/family background. However, since the *Access to Medical Reports Act 1988 (AMRA 1988)* will not normally apply to medical reports prepared by an independent occupational doctor (unless the doctor in question happens also to be the employee's GP or specialist), it will be easier for the employer to obtain medical advice by this route.

Despite the absence of obligations under the *AMRA 1988* in these circumstances, the employer will still need the employee's consent before a medical examination can take place. The easiest way to procure this consent is via a clause in the contract of employment that imposes an express obligation on the employee to agree to be examined by an employer-nominated doctor on request and to allow the resultant report to be disclosed to the employer. Any attempt to force an employee into a medical interview or examination with an occupational doctor that is not authorised by the contract of employment is likely to constitute a breach of contract (see **5.7** above). Despite that, it is open to the employer to simply ask the employee for their consent at the time medical evidence is being sought, even if no clause exists in the contract of employment. The employee may be quite at ease with such a request and may even welcome the opportunity to be examined by an independent doctor who can then provide an objective opinion on their condition.

Dealing with lack of co-operation on the part of the employee   5.34

As mentioned above, the employee has the statutory right to refuse to give their consent for the employer to apply to their GP or specialist for a medical report, and the employer must accept and respect any such decision.

Equally, if there is no clause in the employee's contract obliging them to agree to be examined by an occupational doctor upon the reasonable request of the employer, the employer may be unable to obtain medical advice from this source either.

If, on the other hand, the employee's contract contains a clause obliging them to agree to be examined by an occupational doctor at the request of the employer, and if they nevertheless refuse to comply with a reasonable request to that effect, the employer may have grounds on which to discipline or even dismiss the employee. This will depend largely on the wording of the employee's contract. Discipline and/or dismissal will be possible only if there is a clear statement in the contract that a breach of the rules in this respect will be regarded as a disciplinary offence leading to a warning or dismissal (as the case may be).

Where the employer is unable to obtain medical evidence on account of the employee's lack of co-operation, they will have no option but to base any decision about the employee's continuing employment and rehabilitation on whatever facts are available at the time. In these circumstances, the employee should be appraised of this fact and invited to reconsider whether they wish to agree to be examined by an occupational doctor or consent to a report being sought from their GP. Clearly no unfair pressure should be exerted on the employee, but they should nevertheless be clearly and reasonably informed of any possible consequences of their refusal to co-operate, for example if dismissal on grounds of ill health absence is being considered, or if the lack of medical advice makes it impossible for the employer to determine whether or not a particular workplace adjustment would be appropriate. Normally it is in the interests of both the employer and employee for medical advice to be provided.

Dismissal on Grounds of Sickness Absence or Unsatisfactory Attendance 5.35

Where there is no prospect of rehabilitation and the employee's condition is not expected to improve in the foreseeable future, and where there is no early retirement or PHI provision available to the employee, the employer may ultimately have to consider terminating the employee's employment on the grounds of lack of capability. This course of action should, however, only be contemplated after all other options have been exhausted and medical advice points clearly to the likelihood of the employee not recovering sufficiently to be able to resume work in the foreseeable future.

All employers should devise, implement and apply clear and transparent procedures for termination of employment in a range of circumstances, including ill health absence and attendance. Thus it will be possible for the employer to successfully defend any claim for unfair dismissal so long as the procedures have been followed.

Where dismissal on grounds of lack of capability may be fair 5.36

An employer who decides to dismiss an employee on grounds of long-term sickness will have a potentially fair reason for dismissal. This is because ill health falls under the heading of 'capability', a category which is included in *section 98* of the *Employment Rights Act 1996* as a potentially fair reason for dismissal. It may seem harsh to some to realise that genuine ill health can lead to an employee losing their job, but this harsh effect needs to be balanced against the employer's genuine need to run their business. Few businesses could withstand frequent or long-term employee absences indefinitely as they will need to ensure the work gets done on a regular and reliable basis.

Despite the potential fairness of dismissal on the grounds of genuine ill health, if the employee has a minimum of one year's continuous service, they will have the right to take an unfair dismissal claim to an employment tribunal. It will therefore be very important for the employer to act reasonably and follow proper procedures in carrying out the dismissal. This is because having a valid and potentially fair reason to dismiss an employee is not the only criterion that the tribunal will consider when judging a claim for unfair dismissal. The tribunal will also assess whether or not the employer acted reasonably in treating the reason as sufficient to justify the penalty of dismissal, and in particular whether fair procedures were followed prior to dismissal.

There is no guidance in statute as to the time period after which it may be fair to dismiss an employee who is absent from work due to ill health. The key question for the employer to answer is whether, in all the circumstances, it is reasonable for them to wait any longer for the employee to recover and resume working on a regular and reliable basis. This in turn will depend on a number of factors such as:

- the size and resources of the employer's business;

- the level of seniority and degree of specialism of the employee's job;

- the feasibility of employing a temporary replacement to cover the employee's work;

- the degree of disruption that the employee's absence is causing the business;

- any adverse impact of the employee's absence on their colleagues;

- the length of the employee's absence to date;

- the nature and pattern of any previous absences; and

- the likelihood of the employee being able to return to work in the near future.

Thus in the case of a small organisation that is experiencing severe difficulties as a result of the absence of a key employee (for example the financial accountant responsible for invoices and wages), dismissal may be contemplated after a relatively short period of time, particularly if it is clear from the medical evidence that the employee is unlikely to recover and resume work in the near future. In contrast, a large organisation would have difficulty justifying a speedy dismissal of a junior administrative employee if other employees could readily cover that person's workload or a temporary worker could be drafted in from an employment agency.

Normally, dismissal should be contemplated only as a last resort, ie once all other options have been fully considered and found to be untenable. Even in these circumstances, the employer must still follow certain fundamental procedural steps, namely they must:

- review all the medical evidence thoroughly and take it into account when considering whether to terminate the employee's employment;

- write to the employee to advise them of the fact that termination of employment has become a possibility;

- (if the employee is well enough) set up a meeting (at the employee's home if this is acceptable to the employee) to discuss the prospect of termination, the reasons why the employer believes this has become necessary and to seek the employee's views on this;

- give the employee the right to be accompanied at the meeting by a colleague or trade union official;

- at the meeting explain the facts to the employee, ie why the employer considers that termination is now the only reasonable option;

- consider any representations made by the employee, and whether there are any alternatives to termination, for example if alternative work is available that the employee could do;

- if termination goes ahead, give the employee their full period of notice (with pay);

- inform the employee of their right to appeal against the decision to terminate; and

- keep full records of all discussions.

When dismissal on grounds of unsatisfactory attendance may be fair 5.37

Unsatisfactory attendance can be a fair reason for dismissal whether or not the root cause of the employee's absences is genuine ill health. The general principles applicable to the fairness of a dismissal on account of unsatisfactory attendance are similar to those that apply to a dismissal for long-term ill health absence. This means that there must be a substantial reason justifying dismissal and fair and reasonable procedures must be followed. In this case, the reason for dismissal may be either lack of capability (ill health) or 'some other substantial reason' (unsatisfactory attendance).

Once again, where the dismissed employee brings a claim for unfair dismissal to an employment tribunal, the tribunal will examine not only the reason for dismissal, but also whether the employer acted reasonably in dismissing the employee, taking into account all the circumstances of the individual case. The relevant circumstances will include:

- the total number of days and the number of separate occasions on which the employee was absent;

- the reason(s) for the employee's absences;

- the amount of genuine disruption or difficulty caused by the employee's frequent absences;

- the likelihood of any improvement in attendance in the foreseeable future;

- whether the frequent absences were caused by an underlying medical condition, and if so whether appropriate medical evidence has been fully taken into account by the employer;

- whether appropriate warnings have been given to the employee in relation to unsatisfactory attendance;

- whether the employee has been clearly informed that continuing unsatisfactory attendance would lead to dismissal;

- whether, prior to dismissal, the employee was invited to a meeting to discuss their absences and given a fair opportunity to put forward any representations or mitigating factors;

- whether the employee was afforded the right to be accompanied at the meeting by a colleague or trade union official; and

- whether the employee was given the right to appeal internally against the decision to terminate their employment.

Prior to taking the decision to dismiss, the employer should:

- carry out a thorough review of the employee's attendance record and the reasons for the absences;

- write to the employee to advise them of the fact that termination of employment is being considered and why the employer believes that unsatisfactory attendance may be grounds for dismissal (including with the letter a summary of the employee's absence and attendance record);

- arrange a meeting with the employee to discuss the employer's proposal to terminate employment and to allow the employee to make representations;

- give the employee the right to be accompanied at the meeting by a colleague or trade union official;

- consider once more whether there are any alternatives to termination or whether to allow the employee a further defined period of time to improve their attendance;

- if termination goes ahead, give the employee their full period of notice (with pay);

- inform the employee of their right to appeal against the decision to terminate; and

- keep full records of all discussions.

Policies and Procedures   5.38

All employers should draw up and implement clear procedures for:

- dealing with long-term sickness absence;

- dealing with unsatisfactory attendance, including the problem of frequent, persistent, short-term absences;

- referral to occupational health specialists; and

- termination of employment in a range of circumstances, including ill health absence and attendance (see **5.35** above).

Devising a policy on sickness absence   5.39

Since sickness absence can cause major problems both for the employer and for the absent employee's colleagues who may be required to take on additional work, it is important for the employer to devise and implement effective policies and procedures for managing sickness absence and attendance.

A sickness absence policy should start by making a broad statement about the employer's general approach towards sickness absence. The statement should make it clear that the employer will provide support to any employee who is genuinely sick and will endeavour to put in place appropriate measures to facilitate the employee's rehabilitation.

Drawing up a policy on sickness absence is important so that employees know that management takes the issue of attendance and absence seriously, and so that they can feel confident that they will not be abandoned or penalised in any way if they are absent from work as a result of genuine sickness. A policy is also important to ensure that line managers are aware of their duties and responsibilities towards their staff.

A policy on sickness absence, and any associated procedure, should cover the following issues:

- a statement outlining the employer's general approach towards absence and attendance;

- definitions of short-term and long-term sickness absence;

- the levels of sick pay (both statutory and contractual) that employees can expect to receive, and any conditions associated with payment;

- any provision of benefit under a permanent health insurance scheme;

- the role of occupational health staff;

- a statement that employees are obliged under the terms of their contracts of employment to agree to be examined by an occupational doctor at the employer's reasonable request;

- the employer's approach towards redeployment;

- the availability of ill health retirement, the terms of eligibility and the way in which benefits are calculated; and

- any provision for termination of employment on grounds of incapacity for work, ill health absence or unsatisfactory attendance.

Model policy on long-term sickness absence   5.40

It is the Company's policy to provide reasonable support to employees who are genuinely sick and unable to come to work. In the case of long-term sickness absence (defined as four weeks or more), the Company will pay occupational sick pay (see below) and endeavour, in discussion with the employee, to put in place appropriate measures to facilitate the employee's rehabilitation.

As part of this policy, employees will (subject to a limited number of exceptions listed below) continue to be paid full or part-salary for defined periods of time whilst absent. Specifically, the Company will pay employees their normal basic rate of pay [exclusive of overtime/allowances] during periods of sickness absence of up to [*define period of time*]. This will be followed by a period of [*define period of time*] at half pay.

An employee will not be entitled to occupational sick pay in the following circumstances:

• they have been employed for less than [three/six/twelve] months;

• they have failed to comply with the notification requirements imposed by the Company;

• they have failed to provide a medical certificate to cover their absence;

• they have refused without good reason to attend a medical examination with an occupational doctor at the reasonable request of the Company;

• they have made misleading or untrue statements or produced false documents concerning their condition or fitness to work; or

• disciplinary proceedings are pending against them.

It is a condition of all employees' contracts that they agree, if asked by the Company, to attend a medical examination by an occupational doctor nominated (and paid for) by the Company and to allow the doctor to provide a medical report to the Company.

The Company also operates a permanent health insurance scheme which will provide defined financial benefit to employees who are off work due to sickness for longer than [*define period of time*]. Full details of the scheme are available from …

Under the Company's occupational pension scheme, employees over age [ ] who are members of the scheme and who are incapacitated and unable to work may opt for ill health early retirement. Full details of the scheme are available from …

(cont'd)

An employee who is absent from work long-term will have their position reviewed every three months. Ultimately, if there is little prospect in the longer term of the employee recovering sufficiently to resume working, it may be become necessary from a business perspective to consider termination of employment. In these circumstances, the Company will follow its normal capability termination procedures. The Company therefore reserves the right to terminate the employment of any employee who has been absent from work due to sickness for a period of time in excess of [*define period of time*].

Alternatively, if the employee is medically fit to work generally but unable to perform their normal job duties (for example if their job involves heavy physical work or is particularly demanding in some way), the Company has the right to offer the employee redeployment in another job (if a suitable job is available). The Company will consult fully with the employee before any decision is taken on redeployment.

Any employee who has queries on any aspect of this policy should consult [*name of senior person*].

Devising an attendance procedure   5.41

Employers are not expected to tolerate an employee's frequent, short-term absences indefinitely, and, irrespective of the genuineness of the reasons for an employee's absences, the absences should be properly managed and controlled. It will be helpful for employers to formulate and implement an 'attendance procedure'. A well drafted attendance procedure will help managers manage short-term absence fairly and efficiently, whilst ensuring consistency throughout the organisation.

Model attendance procedure   5.42

Whilst the Company understands that there will inevitably be some sickness absence amongst employees, it must also pay due regard to its business needs. If an employee is frequently and persistently absent from work, or is absent for a lengthy period (albeit for genuine reasons), this can damage efficiency and productivity, and place an additional burden of work on the employee's colleagues.

The overall purpose of this procedure is to encourage satisfactory levels of attendance whilst at the same time allowing the Company to deal fairly, consistently and effectively with any employee whose attendance falls short of what is acceptable. This in turn will ensure that the Company's business interests are not prejudiced as a result of employees' frequent absences from work. The Company thus aims to strike a reasonable balance between the reasonable pursuit of its business needs and the genuine needs of employees to take occasional periods of time off work because of sickness or other legitimate reasons.

This procedure is intended to deal with absences from work due to both ill health and to other reasons that are not on account of a statutory or contractual entitlement. Absences that are not covered by this procedure include approved holiday leave, maternity, paternity, adoption and parental leave, time off to care for dependants and time off for other statutory reasons, eg public duties. Furthermore, pregnancy-related absences will be discounted and any absence due to an employee's disability will be reviewed separately and may also be discounted.

It is open to management to use their discretion to discount from the procedure any individual absence, but such discounting should be done only if the particular circumstances clearly justify an exception being made. Such circumstances should be recorded.

The procedure is structured in four stages comprising three warnings followed by dismissal.

Stage 1

If, during any twelve-month period, an employee is absent from work for fifteen working days (or more), or on five separate occasions, the employee will be interviewed following which a stage 1 warning for unsatisfactory attendance will be issued and placed on the employee's file.

Stage 2

Following a stage 1 warning, if the employee is absent from work at any time during the following six months for five working days (or more) or on three separate occasions, the employee will again be interviewed following which a stage 2 warning for unsatisfactory attendance will be issued and placed on the employee's file.

Stage 3

Following a stage 2 warning, if the employee is absent from work at any time during the following six months for five working days (or more) or on three separate occasions, the employee will again be interviewed following which a stage 3 warning for unsatisfactory attendance will be issued and placed on the employee's file.

Stage 4

If at any time during the period of six months following a stage 3 warning, the employee is absent from work for five working days (or more) or on three

(cont'd)

separate occasions, the employee will again be interviewed following which they will be dismissed.

The employee will have the following rights under the procedure:

- to be given written details of their absence record during the previous six or twelve-month period (as appropriate);

- to be invited in writing to attend an interview under the attendance procedure at not less than one week's notice;

- to be permitted to bring a colleague or trade union official to any interview under the attendance procedure (if they wish);

- to put forward any representations or mitigating factors in relation to their absences at the interview;

- to be given written confirmation of the outcome of the interview;

- to lodge an appeal against any warning under the attendance procedure, or against dismissal, and have the appeal dealt with objectively and fairly.

If, following a warning at stage one, two or three, the employee's attendance is satisfactory for the following six-month period, the employee will revert to the previous stage in the procedure.

Internal and external referral procedures   5.43

All employers should, as part of their overall absence management policy, operate a procedure that allows them to refer an employee to an occupational health specialist at their discretion. This will enable the employer to obtain objective information about the employee's fitness to work, general capabilities and any adjustments that the employer could usefully make to support the employee or facilitate early rehabilitation.

Model policy on referral to an occupational doctor   5.44

The Company retains the services of an occupational doctor. It is the Company's policy to refer any employee who is absent from work due to sickness for longer than four weeks to the occupational doctor for a preliminary examination and report, and to make further referrals at regular intervals as the Company deems appropriate. The Company also reserves the right to refer employees to occupational health where their absences, although shorter than four weeks, have been frequent or where (in the Company's view) there are any other reasonable grounds for seeking advice on the employee's health and fitness to work.

It is a condition of all employees' contracts that they must agree, if asked by the Company, to attend a medical examination by an occupational doctor nominated (and paid for) by the Company and to allow the doctor to provide a medical report to the Company.

If an employee refuses without good reason to agree to attend a medical examination with an occupational doctor, this will constitute a disciplinary offence under the Company's disciplinary procedure. This will lead to disciplinary action being taken against the employee up to and including dismissal.

Chapter 6
Absence Management and Reporting

Introduction   6.1

This chapter provides a general overview of employee absence from an organisational rather than an individual employee perspective. It offers an understanding of the trends in employee absence, including possible triggers, and the trends in management action gleaned from research into solutions and interventions that have proved effective within organisations.

Guidance is provided towards an understanding of the core issues through discussion of data collection, analysis, reporting and OH survey tools, and the taking of effective action through identifying, monitoring and addressing these issues.

What Absenteeism Means for an
Organisation   6.2

There is a substantial body of research into absenteeism. However the subject has remained a largely unrecognised or hidden problem within many organisations, something which has been traditionally viewed as the responsibility of individual line managers or HR specialists. It is only recently that absence management has achieved visibility in the broader management context, as a key contributor to improved productivity in the UK economy.

The first step in understanding the nature of attendance and absence in all organisations is to develop some broad and general indicators and measure these. Increasingly, absence management is being seen as directly linked to organisational productivity and efficiency. Accordingly, it is an important management issue – not just for the HR department, but for the whole organisation.

The management of employee absence has a number of dimensions that need to be specified at the outset. There are two quite distinct types of absence.

Short-term absence   6.3

For the purpose of this chapter, we define short-term absence as that which occurs either as a result of minor illness or injury, or other cause. Short-term absence is usually for a period of five days duration or less. It accounts for up to

80 per cent of total incidences. The 2001 Chartered Institute of Personnel and Development (CIPD) survey found that in relation to short-term absence, genuine illness and accidents accounted for between 50 per cent and two-thirds of all recorded absence (*Employee absence: A survey of management policy and practice,* CIPD, London, 2001).

In all cases, regardless of whether illness or injury is disclosed, the root cause of absence may be the result of low job satisfaction or poor management within an organisation (Bennett H, 'Employee commitment: the key to absence management in local government?' *Leadership and Organization Development Journal,* Vol 23, No 8, pp430–441, 2002).

Long-term absence   6.4

Long-term absence accounts for the remaining 20 per cent of total spells of absence. However, while long-term absence only accounts for a very small percentage of total cases, it is likely to account for up to 70 per cent of the costs associated with absences and 55 per cent of working days lost (*A strategic approach to managing incapacity and long-term ill health, Managing absence in the workplace effectively,* Accor services Family Life Solutions, Unpublished document, 2004).

It is apparent that the UK is lagging behind other countries in the pro-active management of long-term illness and injury. The potential for active early intervention, and rehabilitation programmes to assist employees to return to work, is gaining visibility, in the first instance in the private health insurance industry.

Statistics – a UK profile of workplace injury   6.5

In May 2004, the HSE website (hse.gov.uk/statistics/index) quoted the following statistics:

- There were 226 fatal workplace injuries in 2002/03, a rate of 0.79 per hundred thousand workers;

- In 2002/03, employers reported 154,430 other injuries, a rate of 614.1 per hundred thousand employees; and

- In 2001/02 an estimated 2.3 million people in Great Britain were suffering from an illness which they believed was caused or made worse by their current or past work.

'In 2000–02 an estimated 40 million working days were lost overall, 33 million due to work-related ill health and 7 million due to workplace injury' (home page: http://www.hse.gov.uk/statistics/, April 2004).

Absenteeism trends and costs   6.6

The following section provides a brief summary of some key features and trends associated with absenteeism in the UK as well as a discussion about the direct and potential indirect costs which accrue from it.

General UK trends relating to absence   6.7

The following trends are apparent across the range of available data sources related to the characteristics of absence:

- frequent, short-term absences are more common in younger employees;

- absence rates are generally higher amongst new starters;

- older workers have less frequent absences, however the spells of absence are generally longer;

- females have higher rates of absence than males;

- a high percentage of absences come from a small proportion of the work-force;

- 'conscientiousness' is the strongest predictor of job performance and also low absenteeism (Evans and Walters, p40, 2002);

- past attendance records and frequency of absence is a positive predictor of future absence behaviour;

- absence is generally higher in large, centrally focussed organisations; and

- short-term absences are spread evenly across the week, not only Monday to Friday as is the popular belief.

UK disability trends relating to absence:

- stress, depression or anxiety and musculoskeletal disorders accounted for 13.4 and 12.3 million days respectively-average annual days lost per case for stress, depression or anxiety (29.2 days per case) was higher than for all work-related illness (home page: http://www.hse.gov.uk/statistics/, April 2004).

UK industry and occupational trends relating to absence:

- manual workers have higher absence levels than office workers;

- highest absenteeism is found in the food, drink and tobacco sectors (13.4 days per annum) whilst the lowest is found in the consulting industry (4.7 days per annum);

- the gap between public sector absence (8.9 days-a-year at a cost of £637 per employee) and private sector absence (6.5 days at a cost of £466 per employee) is significant (an annual absence survey released by the

Confederation of British Industry (CBI) and AXA PPP healthcare in April 2004);

- Non-manual workers (5.5 days per employee) have significantly lower rates of absence in comparison to manual workers (8.4 days per employee); and

- smaller companies (organisations with less than 50 staff) have less absence (averaged 4.9 days) in comparison to larger companies (organisations with over 5,000 employees averaged 9.3 days per employee).

Costs of absenteeism 6.8

Research has been conducted into some of the indirect costs associated with absenteeism, including loss of productivity, and the cost and effort associated with procuring and training replacement staff. Estimates which include these quantifiable indirect costs effectively almost double the cost of absenteeism reported. While the direct costs of employee absence are estimated to be between £466 and £637 per employee, the CBI estimated in 1999 that indirect costs inflated absenteeism costs for employers to approximately £1,092 per employee per year.

Indirect costs which are more difficult to measure include potential discontinuity or disruption to the workplace, efficiency impacts due to work interruptions, poor staff morale and potential additional supervisory requirements associated with staff absences (Hawkins R, Comcare, *Occupational Stress – A Strategic Approach*, Conference paper Occupational Health and Safety: Future Directions for a Safer Workplace, Sydney, 3–4 March 1994). In addition, absenteeism may generate other less tangible, but nevertheless significant costs. These include difficulties of maintaining effective customer relationships, the potential for inconsistent advice or service to customers, and increased workload or demands placed on other staff members to manage these issues.

From an organisational perspective, other costs which are directly attributable to absenteeism include the cost of specialist HR support staff and the requirement for managerial intervention. In the case of long-term absences as a result of illness or injury, costs can also accrue from increased insurance premiums and the requirement for legal representation.

Costs associated with absenteeism are not restricted to employers. Individual employees may also incur costs as a result of illness and injury which affects their ability to work. These include additional medical expenses incurred as a result of illness, reduced wages and in some cases, loss of future earnings. There are also likely to be other economic impacts associated with absenteeism which could include an increased requirement for community and welfare services, and increased pension expenditure, coupled with a reduction in taxation contributions as a result of lost wages.

When considered together, the total cost of absenteeism, both at an employer level and across the UK economy, are significant and have been highlighted as a critical issue in recent studies on labour productivity.

Case study 8

The Institute for Employment Studies (IES) 'Costing Sickness Absence' report's main findings included that:

- organisations are ill-equipped to form a comprehensive view of their absence costs;

- between two and sixteen per cent of an employers annual salary bill may be spent on absence;

- numbers of part-time staff, age profile, occupational mix of employees and location were key factors affecting the variability of absence costs; and

- the impact of long-term disability insurance (LDTI) on costs is only effective in combination with an effective management strategy.

(Bevan S and Hayday S, 'Costing Sickness Absence', The Institute for Employment Studies, Report 382, 2001.)

The IES research on tools to cost absence and other labour flows, in the same report, raised the following points:

- checklists rely predominately on identifiable direct costs;

- the salary element of costs doesn't account for some 'on-costs';

- no allowance is made for performance differential between leavers and their replacements or 'depreciation' of human assets; and

- no account is taken of lost productivity among co-workers of a leaver or absentee.

Additionally sometimes short-term financial benefits result through an individual incidence of turnover or absence.

Issues for Management Attention   6.9

Whilst there is a vast array of likely triggers for absenteeism, the following section outlines some of the major organisational trends relating to absence, and their effects on organisations.

In the CBI press release for their most recent absence and labour turnover survey, Dr Mark Simpson, AXA PPP Healthcare Director of Occupational Health Services, said:

> 'The lack of progress in reducing long term absence is deeply disturbing. It continues to account for around five per cent of cases and as much as

one third of time off sick. Yet only half of people responsible for managing absence have ever been shown how to do it. When well established tools such as early assessment and rehabilitation can help people return to work, it seems an enormous waste not to employ them.'

Workforce management and staffing issues   6.10

In industries where specialist professional skills and qualifications are required to sustain operations, the impact of absenteeism on workforce management can present some significant challenges. Health and emergency services are particularly affected in this area. In order to maintain staffing at acceptable levels, it is often necessary to engage additional contracted staff or require core staff to work additional hours at overtime rates.

The former approach results in increased service delivery costs, additional training and supervisory overheads, and potential compromise to service continuity and quality. The latter approach is limited by core staff availability and may, in the longer-term, result in exacerbating staff shortages, due to core staff fatigue and stress as a direct result of additional workload pressures.

Case study 9

A study funded by the Royal College of Nursing found that the effects of nurse absence can cause significant impact on quality and continuity of patient care and increased costs of service delivery. The study demonstrated that short-term absence is problematic in nursing and there appears to be a link between absenteeism and job satisfaction, stress and workload issues. The study concluded that the problem of nurse absence is such that organisational staffing levels need to be planned to accommodate some level of absenteeism to avoid service discontinuity (Seccombe I and Buchan J, 'Managing Nurse Absence' *Health Manpower Management* Vol 21 No 2 pp3–12, 1995).

The use of agency nursing staff, to provide cover for permanent staff absences and skills shortages, can increase costs by more than 150 per cent. James Grabham, a health management professional suggests that total staff costs can increase from approximately £14 per hour for in-house staff to up to £35 per hour for agency nursing staff including overheads, depending on the agency used. In addition, there is also the payment to the employee who is absent.

Employee morale and commitment issues   6.11

In industries where employee morale and commitment appear to be low the impact of absenteeism can be substantial. Studies into occupational stress have pointed to the occurrence of avoidance behaviour as a self-management strategy, which employees use to handle occupational stress and other work-related illness or injury. Avoidance behaviour involves taking recreational or sick leave – a 'mental health day' – without necessarily disclosing the nature of the illness or injury.

A psychological contract is 'an individual's beliefs regarding the terms and conditions of a reciprocal exchange agreement between that person and another party' (Robinson S L and Rousseau D M, 'Violating the psychological contract: not the exception but the norm', *Journal of Organisational Behaviour*, Vol 15, pp246, 1994).

The psychological contract established with an employee can vary significantly according to the following attributes (Bennett H, pp430–441, 2002):

- a purely functional relationship which is based on the provision of services in exchange for an agreed remuneration and benefits package;

- an individual's desire to identify or affiliate; and

- values congruence, which implies that an individual has internalised their employer's organisational values.

While ideally organisations may strive to develop values congruence with all employees, this is neither realistic nor desirable. It is important however, for organisations to recognise these attributes and understand the nature of the psychological contract they have with their employees. In doing so, it is possible to understand and evaluate the impact of proposed organisational changes and target reinforcement of desirable behaviours to each attribute of the psychological contract.

Employee commitment or attachment to their employer and its impact on their patterns of attendance and contribution to the organisation has been researched extensively. The most frequent violations of the psychological contract relate to reward and career in particular to training and development, pay and benefits, and promotional opportunities leading to feelings of de-motivation, anxiety and stress (Robinson, Rouseau, p246, 1994).

Case study 10

A survey conducted across local government organisations in Northern Ireland investigated the relationship between employee commitment and employee absence. Absenteeism has been identified as a major cause for concern for local government in Northern Ireland. The context for the study included recognition of the continual change that has been a feature of local government organisations over the past few years. Despite this, the study found that many local government organisations were perceived as 'over managed and under-led' (Bennett H, 2002) resulting in employee distrust and low morale. The net effect of this has led to increased employee stress, which in turn has translated into higher levels of absenteeism.

Sickness culture issues 6.12

Conventional absence management approaches have tended to concentrate on 'sickness'. However, there is considerable evidence to suggest that individual employees respond differently to illness. In the case of minor illness or injury, employees make an active choice to attend work or to be absent, despite apparent minor illness.

Medicalisation of absence management occurs due to the requirement to substantiate absence with a medical certificate, from a general practitioner, after a defined period. Concerns have been expressed about the role of the general practitioner in this process and the validity of the 'sick note'. There are plans by the Government to alter the system for obtaining 'sick notes' to redirect employees to OH physicians.

Although a 'sick note' from an employee's general practitioner is an advisory document, many employers are loathe to investigate the nature of an employee's illness or to query the recommendations. Medicalisation of absence management is seen in some quarters as problematic and misleading, potentially disempowering line managers from taking an active role in assisting an employee to return to work.

Dr Michael O'Donnell, Chief Medical Officer and Head of Medical Services at UNUM provident believes that:

> 'in spite of the explosion of medical knowledge in the last 50 years, more people of working age than ever before are considered to be too incapacitated to work. Doctors appear to have become worse at treating illnesses as they have got better at treating diseases. In my view for most cases of long-term incapacity the issues preventing a return to work have little to do with the initial reason for going off sick, and have more to do with self-confidence and the perceived unhelpfulness of employers'.

Case study 11

The Bosch income protection scheme, managed by UNUM provident experienced an increasing claims trend since 1997 with a corresponding escalation in premiums. Rehabilitation intervention was required to retain employees with long periods of absence and to make modifications to their workplace or duties to retain them as valuable HR and skills within the company.

Knowledge leakage issues 6.13

Increasingly, many organisations are recognising the costs associated with loss of corporate knowledge or memory, on their core business operations, through absenteeism. Most organisations operate, at least to some degree, on the basis of the willingness of their employees to contribute their personal knowledge of systems and processes, specific skills, experience and judgement, towards fulfilling the requirements of their job. In a majority of industries, this resource is vital to efficient operation and the ability of the organisation to achieve its objectives.

Both short-term and long-term absenteeism erode the ability of organisations to access this (largely tacit) resource, in the form of core corporate knowledge. Furthermore, absenteeism which is the result of poor morale or low employee trust, may negatively affect the likelihood of employees, even when they are at work, voluntarily to contribute ideas and suggestions, proactively to solve problems, or develop workarounds to operational issues in their work environment.

A recent study by the Cornell University Institute for Health and Productivity Studies has identified the concept of 'presenteeism' as the phenomenon where employees continue to work, despite suffering health issues which reduce their productivity. The study suggests that 'presenteeism' may contribute to 60 per cent of the cost of employee illness.

Case study 12

ARUP is a global firm of consulting engineers, providing engineering design, planning and project management services in all areas of the built environment and considers 'knowledge leakage' to be a key issue in staff absence and turnover. ARUP is an employer of choice for their industry and the company operates in an environment where engineering skills are in short supply and where competitors are predatory. Innovative engineering development projects are their core products.

Long hours issues   6.14

A recent survey of the nature of the 'long hour's culture' conducted by CIPD, found that 73 per cent of employees working more than 48 hrs per week, did so either most weeks or every week. Ten per cent of respondents had suffered some form of physical problem associated with their work and 17 per cent experienced some metal health problems, such as depression. This survey appears to substantiate concern that one likely cost of the long-hours culture is to be found in increased sickness absence (Czerny A, 'Will the EC let it lie?' *People Management*, Vol 10, pp12–13, 7–8 April 2004).

Case study 13

In 2000, the Department of Education and Employment recognised the need to address the long hours culture when staff consultations conducted revealed that a key issue for staff was that they were working too hard – around 75–80 hours per week, in some instances. The primary concern was the achievement of work-life balance (Rana E, 'Bichard takes the lead in tipping work-life balance'. *People Management*, Vol 6, No 9 13, 27 April 2000).

Bullying and harassment issues 6.15

A British crime survey reported that there are 1.3 million incidents of work-related violence per annum ('Standards will tackle bullying' *Occupational Health*, Vol 54, No 11, 6 November 2002, Reed Business Information, 2002). As a result of the survey, the HSE has developed standards as part of a three-year programme to curb rising number s of claims of harassment and bullying claims.

The first nation-wide survey of workplace bullying was conducted in 2000 and this found that one in ten people had experienced bullying in the previous six months. Findings indicate that bullying was spread evenly across gender, ages and role, between workers and management. The HSE has identified bullying and harassment as significant factors contributing to work-related stress (Seward K and Fahy S, 'Tackling workplace bullies', *Occupational Health*, Vol 55, No 5, 16–18 May 2003).

Bullying is defined as behaviour which can be intimidating, offensive or insulting to an employee. Bullying can occur as the result of a misuse or abuse of power, which undermines or humiliates an employee. Bullying can also apply to corporate behaviour, not just individual actions. A corporate culture which pressures employees to work long hours is equally unacceptable.

Employers have a duty of care to ensure the health and safety of their employees, under the *Health and Safety at Work etc. Act 1974*. This includes management responsibility for developing strategies to deal with bullying and harassment.

Case study 14

An Australian survey conducted in 1993 found that the majority of staff who reported that they had experienced an illness or injury that they attributed to work, had dealt with the problem through sick leave. The research also demonstrated that claimants who did lodge claims for stress-related illness were found to have taken 3.78 times the amount of sick leave in the twelve months before making a claim (34.4 days) compared to non-claimants (9.1 days). Statistically, significant relationships existed between physical assault, harassment and abuse, and conflict and forced relocation, on the one hand, and sick leave and illness on the other (Toohey J, 'Quality of Working Life Project: A study of occupational stress in Commonwealth Government agencies', Commonwealth of Australia, Canberra, 1993).

In *Young v The Post Office [2002] EWCA Civ 661 (CA)* the court awarded damages to an employee who suffered a work-related stress incident after returning to work from a nervous breakdown. The court considered that there had been a breach of the employer's duty of care in effective management of the employees return to work (Seward and Fahy, 2003).

Leadership and management issues 6.16

Increasingly the UK economy is based on service industries, where customer relationships are of critical importance. Competitiveness relies on effective knowledge management and capacity to innovate. Many organisations have failed to grasp the importance of people leadership as core to their overall success. Leadership and management are often rewarded for technical competence and process conformance, rather than effective employee engagement and team work.

In a recent research report entitled 'Job Insecurity and Work Intensification: Flexibility and the Changing boundaries of Work' conducted by the Cambridge University Centre for Business Research, the findings indicate that job insecurity is closely related with a lack of employees trust in management. The research indicated that nearly 50 per cent of employees trusted management 'not at all' (Walsh J, 1999).

> 'Where values and direction are not communicated, you find business decisions that are not aligned to corporate strategy, managers who stamp on the sensitivities of colleagues, wasted resources through duplication, and, increasingly, burnout as a result of over-working. These "hard" results of "soft" behaviours are costing businesses a fortune'

(Brant E and Whitten H, 'School of hard knocks', *People Management*, Vol 9, No 4 55, February 20 2003.).

Case study 15

In 2001, the Institution of Civil Engineers (ICE) recognised that they had a problem with high staff turnover and absenteeism. Attendant issues included staff disenchantment with ICE as an employer, resulting from limited strategic direction, poor integration of activity, resulting in patch-protection and duplication of effort. Staff reportedly did not feel valued or adequately rewarded for the work that they were doing. The ICE has a long-hours culture among key regional staff and there was a strong perception of management as remote and removed from the day-to-day operations. The organisational structure was centrally focussed and strongly hierarchical with conflicting roles and relationships at the senior management level. Their core business, membership services, was besieged by backlogs of work and lack of continuity of relationships. This resulted in significant difficulties in their ability to provide chartered engineer accreditation status. Additionally existing processes and systems, where they existed, were largely tacit, and the organisation was therefore reliant on key staff for the knowledge carried around in their heads.

HR strategy issues   6.17

The way in which an organisation manages its people is likely to have a critical effect on their attendance behaviour. Conversely, organisations that adhere to the notion that employees are managed as 'a cost', generally operate in a rules-based, compliance culture. This is likely to invite an employee culture based purely on functional exchange, rather than an effective psychological contract. As a result, employees are likely to exploit opportunities to gain access to their full entitlements. In addition, they are likely to evaluate the economic benefits and costs associated with continued absence beyond their defined entitlements.

The importance of 'soft skills' – people leadership, communication, negotiation, teamwork, as core skills for leadership and management has been recognised for many decades. These 'soft skills' are fundamental to the bottom line performance of organisations and are core to effective leadership and management performance.

> 'Rising stress, absenteeism and staff turnover are just some of the damaging effects of the trend to ride roughshod over soft skills.'

(Brant E and Whitten H, 2003.)

Case study 16

Research indicates that persistently high absence rates in the public sector are an indication of poor implementation of recommended policies (Dibben, James, and Cunningham, 2000). Issues such as under resourcing, poor systems co-ordination and management uncertainty concerning implementation can render the 'right' absence management policies ineffective (Taylor S, *People Resourcing*, CIPD, 2002).

Organisational health issues   6.18

The IRS (1998) survey of absence management practices indicated that only two-thirds of organisations had access to OH services. Current issues with the provision of OH in the UK include service access, integration and depth and quality of service provision. The Trades Union Congress (TUC) advocates the need to better integrate existing OH and rehabilitation provision.

Recent reviews, including the HSC report 'A strategy for workplace health and safety in Great Britain to 2010 and beyond'; and public, private and voluntary sector stakeholder feedback have highlighted the need for change. The Department for Work and Pensions has made a commitment to providing a framework for vocational rehabilitation and 'to make better use of existing resources'. Additionally the National Vocational Rehabilitation Associations (NVRA) is working with the ENTO, a group of national training organisations to develop national accreditation standards for the rehabilitation profession (TUC website: www.tuc.org.uk, DWP 'Developing a framework for vocational rehabilitation' discussion paper, May 2004).

Case study 17

In 1998, Standard Life Healthcare (SLH) began a programme to make their company 'a great place to work'. Introduction of a portal enables employees to self-assess their health and well being as well as providing access to support and advice. The portal also enables management reporting to inform planning for additional wellness programmes and incentives. The organisation has seen a productivity increase of ten per cent and a drop in staff turnover from 20per cent to nine per cent over the period since the programme was introduced (Weekes S, 'Making staff well-being part of the company culture' *Personnel Today*, Vol 9, November 4 2003).

Organisational change issues   6.19

Most organisations periodically undergo significant changes in the way they do business, either due to market pressures to increase efficiency and reduce costs, or in order to respond to changing market demands or circumstances. Organisational change occurs in a variety of different ways, either through ad hoc initiatives, planned incremental improvements or large orchestrated programmes.

It is important to consider some of the potential environmental factors which may exist, both within the organisation and also in the broader economy that may impact on employee attendance patterns.

Some key internal environmental factors, which result in changes in the nature of work, may be associated with increased absenteeism. These include:

- restructuring;
- the introduction of new technology;
- business process reengineering;
- re-negotiation of industrial awards or work conditions;
- relocation; and
- changes in management regimes or team structures.

Each of these will have an impact on individual employees. When poorly managed, change can create uncertainty and anxiety as it is often perceived by employees to be accompanied by potential upheaval, redeployment or retrenchment.

In all instances, employees are likely to experience progressive changes to the nature of their day-to-day work. Expectations both on the part of the organisation and its employees may also change considerably over time. Formal performance management processes are essential to acknowledge and communicate changed expectations, however many organisations do not pay sufficient attention to this important area. In some instances, organisational expectations and the day-to-day role of individual employees may become seriously dissociated, negatively affecting organisational productivity and individual job satisfaction.

Change which is poorly communicated and implemented can damage the psychological contract between an employer and employee. If management action is perceived to have an impact on explicit reward structures, or to be misaligned with prevailing organisational values, employees may re-evaluate their commitment. It is at this stage that absence may be used as a self-management strategy to deal with stress, disillusionment or to seek out other employment opportunities.

Case study 18

A review of literature conducted for the Australian Taxation Office and the Commonwealth Public Sector Union (CPSU) assessed the impact of organisational change, particularly change which included downsizing or delayering (Union Research Centre on Organisation and Technology, *Downsizing and Organisational Change*, RMIT, Melbourne, 1996).

The review found that although some organisations have successfully reduced staff and implemented highly successful change, as many as 70 per cent of organisations which have downsized have failed to achieve the desired outcomes from their change programmes. The benefits anticipated as a result of downsizing have also failed, in large part, to be achieved. Nearly 50 per cent of firms failed to achieve productivity gains and that this can be largely the result of costs associated with increased staff workloads, poorly trained staff and additional use of consultants.

The review emphasises the need to manage both employees who are displaced as well as those employees who retain their employment, because loss of morale and commitment can be an unintended outcome of poorly managed change.

Effective Management Action Trends 6.20

The CIPD recommend (February, 2003) an action plan towards OH and organisational effectiveness. The action plan should include:

- provision of strong leadership and ensure employee involvement;
- mission statement;
- health and safety policy that addresses prevention, wellness and partnership;
- determine resources and assign responsibilities;
- determine what needs to be done through an auditing process;
- benchmarking;

- plan for improvements, goals and targets; and

- strategy, review and monitoring process and a time-scale.

Recent research by CBI shows absence falling most significantly in firms where senior managers are responsible for absence management, and return to work interviews the most effective absence management tool. Critical success factors in managing absence cover the following dimensions: employee commitment, leadership and management, conditions of employment and organisational health initiatives.

Three key areas for effective management actions are highlighted, namely:

- employee relations – issues which determine the relationship between the organisation and individual employees;

- issues within the control of the organisation – these are issues over which the organisation has control and can actively direct and manage; and

- broader economy issues – these are external issues which are largely outside the control of organisations.

Workforce management and staffing interventions 6.21

Whilst there should be flexible work policies for family friendly workplaces there is also a need to balance generosity of entitlements with a focus on enabling employees to self manage, ie using interventions such as capped discretionary leave (bank of four hours with approval), payback systems, and flexible hours. Some organisations suggest that enabling staff to self-manage their commitments within the expectations of job requirements results in them being more likely to be available if needed in emergencies or out of normal work hours

Case study 19

A number of NHS Trusts are using the development of 'flexible working lives' policies and tighter sickness absence policies in the hope of reducing absence. They are working with the concept that absence for child or carer responsibilities throws out the figures and are issues that can be supported by the health service in an effort to reduce absence and so increase reliability of service.

HSBC, a global bank, has been operating childcare services since 1989. It currently has 100 such services throughout the UK. The bank has also established an in-house working parents' network, which offers advice and support on parenting issues.

'The quality of care in our nurseries is exceptional. The benefits to staff are increased retention, morale, commitment and reduced absenteeism.'

(Higginbottom K, 'A supporting role', *People Management*, pp12–13, 13 June 2002.)

Employee morale and commitment interventions 6.22

Whilst ideally organisations may strive to develop values congruence with all employees, this is neither realistic nor desirable. It is important however, for organisations to recognise these attributes and understand the nature of the psychological contract they have with their employees. In doing so, it is possible to understand and evaluate the impact of proposed organisational changes, and target reinforcement of desirable behaviours for each attribute of the psychological contract.

Employee commitment or attachment to their employer, and its impact on their patterns of attendance and contribution to the organisation, has been researched extensively. The most frequent violations of the psychological contract relate to reward and career, in particular to training and development, pay and benefits, and promotional opportunities leading to feelings of de-motivation, anxiety and stress (Robinson and Rouseau, p246, 1994).

Absenteeism and turnover have been linked with the level of job satisfaction. Job satisfaction can be impacted on by key features of work and influenced by management practices. In particular employees prefer mentally challenging work, equitable rewards, supportive working conditions and supportive colleagues.

Motivation is also a factor that determines individual behaviour. In the event of absence being rooted in employee dissatisfaction or overbearing control a number of preventative actions have been identified as of significance (Huczynski and Fitspatrick, 1989). These include job:

- enrichment;
- work rotation;
- team-working;
- employee participation;
- improving the work environment;
- better training in supervision;
- improved communication; and
- improved developmental opportunities.

Case study 20

Markham, Dow and Scott describe a one-year controlled experiment in the manufacturing sector which aimed to establish whether recognition programmes had an influence on employee attendance patterns. The study concluded that personal recognition resulted in 'significant decreases ranging from 29 per cent to 52 per cent for each quarter's baseline assessment' (Markham, Dow S E, Scott K and McKee G H, 'Recognising good attendance; a longitudinal, quasi-experimental field study', *Personnel Psychology*, Vol 55, No 3, pp639–60, Autumn 2002).

Sickness culture interventions   6.23

Sickness absence relates only to between fifty per cent and two-thirds of all short-term absence, even with the 'medicalisation' of absence management. Absence management must therefore include a broader focus, to include considerations of work-life balance, employee grievance and industrial relations issues.

Recent research is pointing towards the emerging trend on 'attendance' or 'presence management'. This is the notion that the development and maintenance of a healthy work environment provides a more preventative and holistic method of tackling absence problems (Manocha R, 'Well adjusted' *People Management*, Vol 10, pp26–30, 7–8 April 2004).

An alternative approach, taken by increasing numbers of organisations, is implementing 'wellness' schemes, which aim to build on existing OH initiatives to improve the overall health of the workforce.

Case study 21

In 1992 Australia initiated the Quality of Working Life Strategy to include approaches to the way work was organised and people managed and to try and redress the balance of the majority of interventions to date focussing on assisting individuals to cope with stress (Comcare, 1992). It was a multi-faceted strategy covering prevention, rehabilitation and compensation.

Research indicated that there were indicators that organisations might use to assess their quality of working life. These indicators included:

- the way work is organised;
  - safety,
  - job control,
  - job content,
  - workload and pace,
  - work scheduling,
  - social environment,
- the way people are managed;
  - HR,
  - management systems being supportive,
  - participative,
  - defined role and expectations,

(cont'd)

> o   feedback,
>
> o   opportunity for development and promotion,
>
> •   Quality of working life indicators;
>
> o   rates of compensation claims,
>
> o   rates of absenteeism,
>
> o   rates of client aggression,
>
> o   rates of disciplinary and performance procedures,
>
> o   rates of systems breakdown,
>
> o   staff turnover, and
>
> o   rates of grievance reporting, and
>
> o   measures of job satisfaction.
>
> To enable organisations to identify factors in their work systems that have an adverse affect on health and productivity, practical tools were developed. These tools could be integrated with other workplace initiatives related to enterprise bargaining, quality, customer service and best practice.

Knowledge leakage interventions   6.24

The increasing focus on the value of 'knowledge work' has promoted the importance of developing HR strategies that actually manage employees as 'resources' rather than as a cost to the balance sheet. Organisations that adopt HR management approaches, to recognise the value of employees' skills, knowledge and experience, are more likely to invest in their employees and direct effort towards building commitment, and encouraging retention of valued staff.

> ## Case study 22
>
> An integral part of ARUP's HR strategy is to attract and retain high quality staff, evaluate the real cost of losing employees and promote a succession planning interface. ARUP is driven by a strong sense of ethics cascaded down through the organisation from the recruitment and selection process onwards. The company provides a sophisticated competency based appraisal system and career appraisal system with an internal promotion policy which strives to provide simulating career opportunities. In addition, ARUP has an organisational commitment to social responsibility, encouraging staff to participate in projects such as 'engineers for disaster relief'. In a recent staff survey there was a 72 per cent response rate with eight out of ten people being 'proud to work here' and the organisation is considered a highly desirable entry point for young engineers after they finish their academic qualifications. Additionally ARUP have a strong culture of sustainability 'we shape a better world' and were recently featured in *The Sunday Times* top 100 companies survey.

Long hours interventions 6.25

The challenge of dealing with issues relating to the long-hours culture in the UK is somewhat complicated. Two pieces of work completed in 1999 highlight the different perspectives related to perceptions about the long-hours culture. While the surveys agree on the numbers of people working over the 48-hour limit set by the European working directive, they disagree about the reasons behind this practice. *Living for Work*, the survey conducted by the Institute of Personnel and Development (IPD) (Walsh J, 'Studies at odds over root of UK's long-hours culture', *People Management*, Vol 5, page 16, 2 September 1999) found that one in eight workers choose to work long hours because they enjoy their work and that only very few people work long hours because they feel insecure in their employment. A third of managers and professional surveyed said that they were 'self-confessed workaholics' and many attributed their need for additional hours to the inefficiency of their organisation. The survey acknowledges the need for organisations to deal with burnout issues.

The other survey, *Job Insecurity and Work intensification: Flexibility and the changing boundaries of work*, asserts that the drive for productivity is putting pressure on workers and resulting in increased job insecurity and ill health. This research predicts that the long-term effects of the long hours culture 'have worrying implications for employees [and] for the country's future growth rates' (Walsh J, 1999).

Case study 23

In 2000, the permanent secretary of the Department of Education and Employment launched a work-life balance campaign. The campaign included both work-life balance and equity issues and included the introduction of flexible working hours, a bursary scheme to allow high performing employees to build their knowledge and reform to increase flexibility of performance appraisal systems to reward high performers and encourage workplace diversity (Rana E, 2000).

Bullying and harassment interventions 6.26

The Employment National Training Organisation have drawn up standards to deal with bullying and harassment. These standards include investigation of suspected bullying, building a safe and healthy workplace and control measures for dealing with bullying and harassment claims (Reed Business Information, 2002).

The prevention of bullying requires active management attention and the development of strategies to prevent it. There must be a clearly articulated management standard of behaviour, supported by coaching and training so that senior managers can demand appropriate behaviour from all staff.

Case study 24

Dealing with bullying requires the development of effective workplace policies and procedures, as well as clearly articulated processes for dealing with
claims of bullying and harassment. These should include:

- a definition of bullying and harassment and a statement that it is unacceptable behaviour in the workplace;

- defined processes for making a complaint and seeking support;

- a defined process for investigation of a claim, including protection of the
  'victim' of bullying;

- clearly explained consequences for bullying and harassment, including
  disciplinary action and withdrawal from the workplace; and

- procedures for seeking support from an outside, objective party, in the
  event of management harassment.

Leadership and management interventions   6.27

Leadership and management are core determinants of organisational culture and
the behaviour of staff. A key feature of leadership is that it determines the culture
in which teams, and the individuals in them, can contribute fully to achieving the
desired organisational outcomes. Development of a 'high performance environment' has been demonstrated to be most effective in developing employee commitment and contribution, hence reducing absenteeism.

Sound leadership involves establishing and maintaining an environment which
enables high performance, including the following attributes (Mink O G, Owen
K Q, and Mink B P, *Developing High Performance People*, pp 58–60, Addison
Wesley, Massachusetts, 1993):

- shared vision and values;

- clear goals;

- enabling processes and systems;

- recognition of productivity and accomplishment;

- the right people;

- rewarding teamwork; and

- feedback and problems solving.

Differentiating leadership and management has been the subject of considerable
research, however Dunphy and Stace provide an elegant description which
includes the attributes of management as:

- planning and budgeting;

- organising and staffing;

- controlling and problem solving; and

- producing a degree of predictability and order.

(Dunphy D and Stace D, *Beyond the Boundaries: Leading and re-creating the successful enterprise*, pp128, McGraw Hill, Roseville, NSW, Australia, 1994.)

Dunphy and Stace contrast this with leadership dimensions including:

- establishing direction;

- aligning people;

- motivating and inspiring; and

- producing change.

From these definitions, it can be seen that both leadership and management are critical to maintaining a healthy, focused organisation, capable of high performance.

Management responses to absenteeism vary significantly in their approach and effectiveness. CBI and IRS survey evidence indicates that most employers operate punitive absence management techniques and believe them to have a degree of effectiveness. However Allen and Torrington (1996) suggest that management signalling they intend to make absence an issue is more significant than the punitive approaches themselves. Punitive absence control measures often fail to distinguish between genuine short-term sickness or care needs and avoidable absence. Hence, these approaches may be perceived by employees as operating unfairly and this may, in turn, undermine the important trust relationship which is critical to fostering employee commitment and contribution.

In UNUM Provident's experience of working with a range of companies both white and blue collar it is clear that a culture that approaches sickness absence with a degree of scepticism cannot expect to benefit from a trusting workforce. Where employers take a disciplinarian approach to sickness absence, employees are less likely to be honest and open about their difficulties and this tends to breed an environment where effective communications between the employer and employee tend to break down and return to work is more difficult to achieve. Employers would benefit from providing very clear guidelines on the expectations of all parties during a period of absence. This would ensure that the employee is fully aware of their responsibilities and the employer takes early action to ensure the most appropriate advice and guidance is sought to support their employee back to work. One very effective tool is the return-to-work interview and by utilising the services of an experienced vocational rehabilitation specialist. On-going support for the employee and employer can be assured.

Case study 25

In response to their difficulties the ICE:

● conducted exit interviews;

● developed a business ethic and culture – 'even though this is a charity, it is necessary to employ business ethics and management techniques';

● improved membership services;

● changed the management structure including changes in staffing at the top and the formation of a presidential team;

● developed a new divisional structure – reduced the number of divisions and introduced a communications division with responsibility for internal and member communications, engaged repositioning, re-branding and matrix management;

● developed a business plan in conjunction with ICE staff and supported this with a strategy and matrix management structure, designed to break down previous 'silos';

● developed a learning strategy; and

● reviewed the staff reward scheme to introduce structure and flexibility.

Staff turnover has reduced by 30 per cent, only three staff members are on long-term sick leave and short-term absence although not measured, is believed to be significantly improved.

HR strategy interventions   6.28

The CIPD recommend that an effective absence management strategy should be based on a written absence management policy, with full and visible top management commitment and in addition to the policy statement, clear absence procedures must set out the detail in employee handbooks. They outline a number of policies to manage and discourage absence:

● absence strategies, policies and targets;

● enhancing the role of the line manager;

● involving employees and trade unions;

● absence monitoring;

● return-to-work interviews;

● establishing trigger-points for extended and recurrent short-term absence;

● absence review and counselling meetings;

- disciplinary procedures; and
- using absence as a criteria for redundancy selection.

The HSE recommend policies be developed in the following areas:

- HR planning;
- job design and re-design;
- recruitment;
- selection;
- induction;
- conditions of service;
- training;
- development;
- career management;
- communication;
- performance management;
- employee relations;
- reward;
- redundancy;
- evaluation;
- organisational change and development; and
- occupational health and safety or welfare.

Case study 26

The HR strategy for ARUP provides a range of short and long-term absence management interventions. ARUP does not consider itself to have an entitlements ethic or particular short-term absence problem. Fourteen staff have been absent over six months out of a UK workforce of 3,500. Staff turnover is low.

- Absence is measured via timesheet information to identify patterns and trends.
- The HR process for managing avoidable absence is linked into performance and disciplinary procedures.
- Line manager undertake informal return to work interviews to identify issues and help develop solutions.

(cont'd)

- Sick leave provisions are very generous.

- Link between absence management and helping improve performance.

- EAP solutions are in place, including counselling and coaching.

- Income protection provision provides early intervention and rehabilitation services. There is a defined process for managing long-term absence and inclusion of line managers in the return to work process with HR support.

- All endeavours are made to provide flexible return-to-work solutions designed to suit the individual.

- Staff experiencing difficulties can expect helpful and supportive HR options and the organisation has a reputation for protecting people.

ARUP HR function have identified increased visibility of absence management to senior management, increased line manager education and early diagnosis and assistance for short-term absentees through the use of an OH function as future developments to their absence management strategy.

Organisational health provision interventions   6.29

The CIPD (2001) absence survey indicated that amongst respondent organisations, approximately 60 per cent involved OH in absence management. OH was seen as the most effective tool for managing long-term sickness.

An EAP can be beneficial as they provide confidential and anonymous counselling on work or personal issues. In-house models provide service staffed by employees within the organisation. External models use external professionals to provide services. Mixed models offer a flexible mix of services.

Rehabilitation is essential to improving opportunities for return to work for employees who have potentially long-term injury or illness. It provides assistance to employers and employees to fully understand the nature and impact of the employee's injury or illness on their ability to return to their current job and minimise the risk of injury exacerbation in the long term. Occupational rehabilitation is directed toward gaining appropriate assistance to enable the employee to return to work at the earliest opportunity, either to their existing employment or to a different one. The IRS (2001) identified the following respondent employer practices:

- phased return to pre-absence duties or hours (90 per cent of respondents);

- medical examination or review of medical reports (88 per cent);

- maintenance of contact with absent employee (88 per cent);

- providing time off to attend medical appointments post-return (84 per cent);

- early intervention to prevent acute conditions becoming chronic – eg physiotherapy, counselling (82 per cent);

- permanently changing or modifying previous tasks (65 per cent);

- providing special equipment or aids (64 per cent);

- permanently altering pre-absence working pattern (62 per cent);

- providing retraining (62 per cent);

- preparation of return-to-work report (51 per cent);

- access to private medical treatment (41 per cent);

- special supervision or mentoring (39 per cent);

- change of work location (39 per cent);

- use of internal redeployment register (33 per cent);

- help with travel to work (28 per cent); and

- providing access to external job placement service (19 per cent).

Critical success factors associated with successful return to work for injured workers are early intervention, keeping in contact with employees and the provision of alternate employment options and suitable duties for return to work.

Case study 27

Bosch income protection scheme claims and premiums became stable over two years even given that their group income protection rates increased by ten per cent. Formalised rehabilitation service agreements, improved communication including six weekly review meetings between the rehabilitation counsellor and HR, and more active intervention in sickness absence have proved key interventions

Adidas commenced a wellbeing programme in 1997 which has reached about 80 per cent of its 450 UK-based employees. The programme has reported impressive results, both to employee physical health and mental attitudes. Trapp cites the example of an employee who underwent a serious heart operation who was able to return to work within three months of the surgery which was 'much sooner than would otherwise have been the case' (Trapp R, 'Fit for the job', *People Management*, Vol 8, No 13 pp48–9, 27 June 2002.

Organisational change interventions 6.30

A CIPD survey found that the economic downturn has contributed to a ten per cent fall in sickness absence (*Employee Absence*, CIPD, 2003). In 2002, the employees took an average of ten days off sick whereas the 2003 survey shows the average to have fallen to an average of nine days absence. Workplace uncertainty, coupled

171

with increasing prevalence of HR interventions, such as return-to-work interviews and absence monitoring, appear to have contributed to the falling levels of absence.

Large-step change initiatives inevitably challenge prevailing organisation values, operating models and roles. Whilst some of these changes may result in increased anxiety or stress levels amongst staff, some may have equally significant consequences by increasing the risk of physical injuries. Holistic change management processes consider organisational culture and values, as well as practical considerations such as OH and safety issues. Impacts on work organisation, roles and responsibilities, management and team structures, and appropriate skill-building form significant components of the design of any significant change process.

The external environment also exerts an important influence on employee morale and commitment, with a resultant impact on absence and attendance patterns. Some examples of this include:

- industry restructure;

- downturns or surges in the economy that change the relative value of particular skills or qualifications;

- the level of competition in the marketplace; and

- geographic or political influences.

Whilst some of these factors will negatively impact on employee attendance, others, such as poor economic outlook, may contribute to higher levels of attendance driven by the increased motivation of employees to retain their employment. Conversely, if the relative value of particular skills alters significantly, and employees feel that their skills are being exploited, they may seek to redress the perceived imbalance by fully utilising non-salary entitlements.

Case study 28

In 2001 Accenture, a global IT consulting company, were faced with a serious economic downturn and were required to drastically cut costs. A one-year sabbatical programme was piloted, which allowed workers to take a year off in return for 20 per cent of their salary and all employee benefits. The scheme has also been offered to employees in Europe and Japan.

Benchmarking   6.31

Comparison with relevant industry benchmarks is a useful guide to assessing an organisation's current performance, however, it should be noted that currently available industry benchmarks may vary in reliability, depending on industry sector and sample size. The actual costs associated with absence in an organisation may provide sufficient impetus to develop a more deliberate and planned approach to absence management.

Developing a measure related to the cost of absence provides a useful starting point to developing a business case. To gain a gross measure of the estimated direct wage costs associated with employee absence is achieved by multiplying the average salary plus overhead costs per employee by the number of days lost through absence. This can be compared with relevant industry benchmarks, available through CIPD or the Work Foundation. There is an easy-to-use calculator for undertaking this calculation available on the website of a major income protection insurer (UNUM Provident: http://www.unumprovident.co.uk/AbsenceCalculator.asp).

Benchmarking data is usually done in one of two ways. Using comparative data, based on discrete single variables eg general absence data by industry sector, industry group, geographic region or organisation size, from CBI or Industrial Society. This is of limited use if there is a preference to benchmark against the best performers or those in the top quartiles.

The second method is to target an organisation for comparison. Competitors, organisations working in related but non-competitive fields or organisations recognised as setting high performance standards may be useful to consider. In the UK voluntary or 'club' benchmarking organisations exist to provide assistance with this process.

Appropriate benchmarking data helps to identify the organisational issues and potential targets for improvement activity. Benchmarking may also inform the determination of absence levels that are tolerable or intolerable for different sectors of the organisation within agreed levels of investment. Internal benchmarking through the publication of results can drive changes to behaviour, however in some instances may lead to abuse or manipulation of the system.

Systematic benchmarking is recommended and should involve sharing qualitative data and information, practices and experiences, and could give leads concerning causes, effectiveness of policy initiatives and strategies to overcome practical difficulties.

Case study 29

Tracey Gazeley, Independent EAP Consultant in association with Health Management Ltd states that the benefit of consultation with your EAP in the benchmarking process is many-fold. A good EAP will have a ROI tool and it will profile the absence costs alongside the cost of retention. Part of the management information from such a service, if consultancy is applied, will be the confidential aggregated industry sector or organisational profiling of other client organisations. The psychosocial risks associated with absence is an area in which an EAP will work hard to influence and the aggregated statistical data will be a powerful tool in the benchmarking process. For instance both the pharmaceutical and telecom industry have, in personal experience, made sound use of benchmarking sector specific and organisational change data. This collated information has been used to influence the shape of programmes prior to implementation in addition to added weight to the management buy-in to such schemes.

Ensuring Active and Effective Reporting   6.32

The following section outlines some of the considerations that should be taken into account in gaining a more detailed understanding of absence and attendance patterns within an organisation. At the outset, it is often useful to establish a 'reference group' or project steering committee to provide input into research design, to provide support for the research process; and to test and validate the research outcomes.

The following are some commonly used steps associated with conducting research:

- establishment of a baseline;

- problem identification and formulation;

- secondary data analysis;

- primary data collection;

- analysis and synthesis of findings;

- validation of findings; and

- preparation of report.

There are many useful texts on research conduct; Davis provides a comprehensive explanation of business research techniques and considerations (Davis D, *Business Research for Decision Making*, 4th Edition, Wadsworth Publishing Company, 1996).

Establishing a baseline-formulae for measuring absence   6.33

Prior to commencing a detailed research process, it is important to establish a baseline for the level and nature of absenteeism within an organisation.

There are three common methods for measuring absence, which are described in detail by Evans and Walters (Evans A, Walters M, *From Absence to Attendance*, pp28–55, 2nd Edition, Chartered Institute of Personnel and Development, London, 2002). These are time loss measures, frequency measures and Bradford factor score. The widely accepted formulae for calculating time lost and frequency measures are described by the Advisory, Conciliation and Arbitration Service (ACAS) (*Absence and Labour Turnover*, ACAS, London, 1999).

1   The time lost measure is calculated as follows.

$$\frac{\text{Number of days/shifts lost (standardised by hours)}}{\text{Total number of days/shifts available}} \times 100$$

Time lost is calculated on the basis of 228 working days per year to enable benchmarking with the CBI. It is important to adjust figures for part-time or part year work.

2   There are two frequency measures.

The first calculates the frequency rate as follows:

$$\frac{\text{Number of spells of absence}}{\text{Total number of employees}} \times 100$$

The second calculates the individual frequency (incidence or prevalence) rate as follows:

$$\frac{\text{Number of employees having one or more spells of absence during a period}}{\text{Total number employed in the period}} \times 100$$

3   Bradford factor.

The Bradford factor is based on an approach devised by the University of Bradford which considers the overall impact of absence on the workplace, noting that frequent, short-term absences are considered to be more disruptive. Points are awarded on a weighted basis to develop an indicator of potential disruption to the workplace.

The Bradford factor is calculated as follows:

points scored = (S × S) × D

(where 's' is the number of spells in a period and 'D' equals total days off for the period). The higher the score, the greater the level of disruption can be predicted from short-term absence.

Evans and Walters suggest that while time lost measures are useful for external benchmarking, frequency measures and Bradford factor scores are more useful for developing internal management policies.

In an extensive review of the literature on absence management, provide a detailed description of a variety of perspectives on some of the critical issues to consider in terms of diagnosis of problems associated with employee absence. It is apparent from this analysis, that the accurate diagnosis of the causes of employee absence is complex, multi-dimensional and subtle. There are no simple predictors of the likelihood of employee absence and hence no simple prescription for dealing with the problem (Evans A, and Walters M, pp28–55, 2002).

Explanations of absence range from single factors as described by Nicholson (Nicholson N, 'Absence behaviour and attendance motivation: a conceptual synthesis', *Journal of management studies*, Vol 14, pp231–252, 1977), such as high frequency absences related to avoidance behaviour, employee adaptation to cultural and behavioural norms within an organisation and economic benefits and costs associated with leave entitlements. Research indicates that the provision of generous sick leave which reduces cost of absence to the employee is a contributor to higher levels of absenteeism (Evans A, and Walters M, pp28–55, 2002).

Throughout the description of the research process, we will follow a specific example.

Example approach to researching absence management
6.34

Organisation X identifies that its time lost measures are significantly higher than the industry benchmark. Further investigation based on frequency measures indicates that absence is related to a small number of long-term absence spells and a high incidence of frequent short-term absences.

Models
6.35

Absence management reporting needs to be customised to meet specific organisational needs and take account of specific organisational influences such as the working environment, job design, organisational culture etc. The key is to understand these influencing dynamics and then provide an appropriate mix of absence management approaches.

Firstly it is important to ask the question 'is our level of absence unacceptable?' and would any investment be proportionate to the cost involved. To answer this question accurate information on the level and characteristics of absence and external benchmarking is required. Typically most organisations have data on direct costs to inform statutory sick pay schemes and for supervisory and resourcing purposes but have difficulty aggregating this local data.

Problem identification and formulation
6.36

It is essential to properly identify and define the problem to be solved, prior to commencing the research. Problem identification and definition is arguably the most important step in any research process.

Problem definition involves a structured approach to development of an hypothesis, based on some preliminary investigation and the testing of the hypothesis against available information. Once the hypothesis is either proven or disproven, it is possible to consider more detailed analysis based on developing an understanding of the symptoms and causes related to the research question.

Example: research question
6.37

Recognising the symptoms:

We have a number of employees who have been on long-term sick leave for over three months. We also have a business issue related to the need to rapidly redeploy staff from one location to another in order to maintain minimum staffing requirements in our customer-facing outlets.

Identifying the problem space:

1   Internal data and information sources:

- profile of long-term injury or illness – including nature of injury or illness, employee role, age, gender, location; and

- profile of absence in customer facing outlets, including frequency, Bradford factor, employee profile, location profile.

2   Developing the problem space:

- customer outlets have recently extended operating hours;

- customer-facing staff have expressed some dissatisfaction with existing processes and systems; and

- improved pay and conditions are an ongoing issue for these staff.

Research question example: *what are the main factors associated with both long-term and short term absence in our organisation?*

Understanding the problem   6.38

Evans and Walters outline four distinct characteristics which inform an understanding of employee absence. These are personal characteristics, issues relating to organisational context, external issues and other related issues (Evans A, and Walters M, pp36–53, 2002).

Personal characteristics which are important to consider in relation to employee attendance include length of service, age, gender and job role. Factors such as personality, personal values and individual attitudes to work can also be important variables in employee attendance. Past absence behaviour is a reliable indicator of future behaviour. Generally, a high proportion of overall absence emanates from a small percentage of the organisations' workforce.

In the category of organisational issues to be considered, work design and work-group norms are important, as is organisational and team culture. Organisational policies and practices can have an important impact on attendance and absenteeism, including the visibility of absence management policies, generous leave entitlements, and benefits packages which reward attendance.

Other factors that are associated with absence include stress and individual frequency of job moves. Absenteeism is often linked to particular leadership style of a supervisor or manager and in some organisations, the level of staff turnover and absenteeism is used as an indicator of poor management as part of a performance appraisal system.

The size of the organisation, as well as work group size can have an important effect on absence, with larger organisations experiencing higher levels of absence across the board.

Important external factors that have been shown to have an impact on attendance behaviour include the prevailing economic and market conditions. In tight economic times, the rate of absenteeism declines markedly.

It is important to acknowledge that between one-third and half of short-term absence relates to genuine illness and accidents (*Employee absence: A survey of management policy and practice*, CIPD, London, 2001). Non-illness absences may be due to travel and transport problems and also to employees' family or carer responsibilities (CBI/ BUPA/MCG, *Managing absence: in sickness and in health*, CBI, London, 1997)

There is no single cause for absenteeism and there is no one solution for developing effective strategies for dealing with the issue. It is important to consider the nature of the organisation, the likely trigger points and then analyse the effects based on these. Some key trigger points can occur during changes to structures, work processes or technology implementations; at significant points in a career such as full professional accreditation or close to retirement age.

Secondary data   6.39

There is generally a wealth of available information which can provide insight into employee absence within most organisations. It is important to make effective use of information that is already available.

Developing a few simple but potent indicators is recommended. This will provide enough information to inform the development of appropriate policies and monitor their effectiveness. Developing effective monitoring will usually be an iterative process, involving initial measures which are refined over time.

A cost-effective starting point involves the use of secondary data from available internal sources, in existing systems and records. It is essential to take into account the purpose for which the data was collected and the likely biases or constraints that may be associated with its use.

Data is generally drawn from existing repositories and sources in the first instance. Research would generally cover:

- internal information including:
  - ○ previous consulting or project reports,
  - ○ employee feedback,
  - ○ surveys,
  - ○ complaints,
  - ○ minutes of IR related meetings,
  - ○ management reports,
- literature review of relevant industry issues; and

- analysis of existing data in current HR and other systems to profile nature of absence issues.

Example: secondary data analysis   6.40

The following data and information is generally available through existing organisation records and data systems:

- workforce demographic data – profile of attendance patterns by:
    - gender,
    - age,
    - job role,
    - salary range,
    - length of service,
    - geographic area,
    - organisational unit,
    - any other relevant criteria that are specific to each organisation,
- nature of absence, short-term or long-term;
- number of certificated absences;
- profile of illness or injury types;
- return to work statistics for long-term sickness;
- number of employees on restricted duties; and
- income protection claims profile and premiums.

Surveys

Surveys provide an effective mechanism for collecting useful additional quantitative and qualitative information:

- from a large number of staff;
- from staff spread over a wide geographic area;
- from staff who wish to provide anonymous feedback; and
- where there are gaps in existing demographic information in existing systems and additional quantitative analysis is required.

There are a range of proprietary employee absence and organisational climate surveys available, which can be customised to accommodate specific organisational issues. Many of these surveys can be used as a basis for internal benchmarking as well as benchmarking with other organisations.

(cont'd)

Alternatively, it is possible to design effective fit-for-purpose surveys to meet specific organisational requirements. Survey design is very important in order to derive relevant, accurate and unbiased information. It is essential that surveys are pilot tested prior to release.

Designing and administering a survey involves some important considerations, namely:

- sample selection:
  - o sample methodology,
  - o sample size,
  - o avoidance of sampling bias,
- mode of survey:
  - o telephone interview,
  - o face-to-face interview,
  - o web or email questionnaire,
- survey design based on data requirements;
- analysis methodology and tool; and
- communications and feedback to participants

Focus groups

Focus groups are often a valuable source of interpretive information. Conducting focus groups is a useful way of gathering cause and effect data, testing hypotheses formulated from secondary data analysis and gaining insights into more subtle issues that may not be apparent from analysis of available secondary data.

Focus groups design should include the following considerations:

- sampling – the options are to have like groups based on:
  - o organisational teams, job roles, or locations, or
  - o mixed groups, based on 'slices' across the organisation of staff from different areas or teams, or from different job roles;
- session structure:
  - o structured focus questions,
  - o large group discussion,
  - o small group sessions reporting back to a plenary forum; and

- data capture:
    - voice recording,
    - whiteboard, and
        - flipchart, and
        - notes recording.

Focus groups provide a wealth of qualitative data and can engage participants in the process. It is important to ensure that mechanisms for collecting and analysing the resulting information are determined prior to the conduct of the sessions. When focus groups are conducted within organisations, it is generally good practice to provide some broad feedback to participants about outcomes resulting from their contribution.

Structured interviews

The use of structured or semi-structured interviews is differentiated from broad survey techniques, as these are generally used to gather specific information, either related to issues identified in secondary data analysis, or to gain the perspective of a particular specialist.

In the majority of research processes, structured interviews are generally conducted with a small number of key stakeholders. The example below demonstrates their effective use.

If embarking on primary data collection, it is important that care is taken to establish appropriate confidentiality and privacy to safeguard research participants. It is also essential to develop a rigorous, predefined analysis methodology for the resultant data before commencing collection.

Primary data collection   **6.41**

Once an analysis of secondary data is complete, it may be appropriate to collect some primary data or information to gain further insights into the research question.

A computerised system is recommended for data processing. This should enable analysis of days lost on an individual, grade, department and occupational group, location, contractual group and manual or non-manual labour basis. Also frequency of number of absence spells, hours of work or average pay. Inclusion of an integrated absence warning system programmed to generate 'flags' to users when certain thresholds or triggers are exceeded is beneficial. In the absence of any or all of these functions data calculations can be done manually or existing data downloaded to more specialised software.

Example: primary data collection   6.42

The HR manager from organisation X decided to develop employ multiple primary data collection techniques to gain a clear understanding of the factors relating to absence across the organisation.

1   An employee survey of ten multiple-choice questions related to employee attitudes to short-term absence. A link to a web-based survey form was emailed to a randomly selected number of customer-facing employees and their managers across the organisation, to provide de-identified data. Data was uploaded into a purpose-designed database enabling analysis and statistical manipulation.

2   A small number of interviews were conducted with key stakeholders, including the Customer Service Manager, the outsourced EAP contractor, a union delegate, the rehabilitation provider and the Chief Finance Officer, who is responsible for employer liability insurance.

3   Four focus groups were held in key locations, each one had customer-facing staff involved in different locations. The focus questions for these groups were identical to the questions in the survey. The groups were asked to work in small groups to discuss each question and report their findings back to a whole group plenary session. Outcomes of the discussions were captured by a combination of participant flip chart recording and voice recorded discussions.

Analysis and synthesis of findings   6.43

Data and information gathered in the research process must be systematically analysed according to recognised statistical and, if appropriate, qualitative methods. Analysis of data and information for decision making must be related to the research design and the purpose for which the data was collected. Davis recommends the following steps for developing a data analysis plan:

1   select appropriate analytical software, including statistical, graphical and publication components;

2   conduct pre-analytical checks to purify and refine data for analysis;

3   decide basic statistical methods for analysis; and

4   identify how the results will be organised and presented.

(Davis D, *Business Research for Decision Making*, 4th Edition, pp332, Wadsworth Publishing Company, 1996.)

Validation 6.44

Once the information and data has been analysed and presented in a format that will inform the relevant decision makers, it is advisable to validate the findings prior to general release. This step can involve a post-analysis quality check with an objective data analyst. It is also advisable to test the results with a reference group or project steering committee.

Identifying trends and patterns of behaviour 6.45

While establishing a baseline is the first important step in identifying trends in behaviour, it is essential to develop a clear understanding of the multiple factors that impact on absence and to develop measures for all proposed interventions. It is also important to make sure that there is an ongoing approach to monitoring absence and attendance behaviour to track trends over time. The climate and characteristics of absence behaviour are constantly changing, and it is only through careful measurement and monitoring that these trends and patterns can be observed. This does not mean that extensive research is required, however routine reporting of HR data and outcomes of return-to-work interviews, along with exit interview results can easily be tracked and maintained.

Within the change context, it is possible to adopt a model or series of models to aid understanding of the change process and allow analysis of activities surrounding this process. There are numerous models for understanding the impact of change, both at the organisational level and at the individual employee level. One such model is the Concerns Based Adoption Model (CBAM) (Adapted from Mink O G, Owen K Q, Mink B P, *Developing High Performance People*, pp29–33, Addison Wesley, Massachusetts, 1993) and subsequent adaptations introduces the concept of Stages of Concern (SOC) and Levels of Use (LOU).

Developing effective interventions 6.46

An effective absence management programme must be tailored to the particular factors affecting individual organisations. The CIPD recommend:

- a clear, consistent and commonly accepted framework for the management of absence encompassing:
  - statement of attendance standards,
  - management commitment,
  - systematic procedures for managing general and problem absence,
  - investigation,
  - counselling,
  - action steps,

- application of organisation-wide absence management principles or initiatives including:

  o   thorough and consistent communication to the whole workforce,

  o   instituting effective recruitment,

  o   selection and induction procedures,

  o   addressing performance management appraisal systems and performance related pay issues, and

  o   addressing issues of employee commitment and motivation through job design and work organisation, and

  o   providing flexible employment policies and OH initiatives.

(Evans A, and Walters M, *Absence to Attendance*, CIPD, 2003.)

Report preparation   6.47

Once the results of the research are completed, it is important to develop a report which is comprehensive and developed to meet the requirements of the intended audience. In general, reports which are targeted to senior management are generally succinct and action oriented. The production of detailed findings may also be required, however it is essential to publish an executive summary with 'headlines' to support easy assimilation of key findings.

Marketing the Change Programme throughout the Organisation   6.48

Establishing an effective, sustainable change to employee absence requires a co-ordinated and well communicated change programme to be implemented.

Effective absence management requires changes to behaviour, both at the employee and management level. At the employee level, successful change relates to achieving individual employee behaviours which are consistent with the fulfilment of their attendance and contribution obligations and responsibilities. In addition, employee behaviour must adhere to workplace OH and safety requirements, and organisational codes of conduct. It should also contribute to the maintenance of a supportive work environment to encourage peers on restrictive duties as a result of workplace injury or illness.

At the management level, behaviour change expectations relate to the ability of supervisors and managers to develop a positive work culture which is based on shared goals, mutual trust and team collaboration. Within this environment, supervisors must demonstrate willingness to offer support to their employees in difficult circumstances and consider flexible work practices or other solutions, when employee needs are genuinely affecting their ability to fulfil their responsibilities. Supervisors and managers need to communicate expectations about workplace attendance effectively and deal with unexplained absence sensitively and firmly, when required. In some of these areas, line managers will require training and support from HR specialists.

The importance of effective communication   6.49

Underpinning all effective change programmes, indeed all effective people management strategies, lies effective communication. Unfortunately, while there is widespread recognition of this aspect of people management, building an effective communication approach and implementing it throughout the organisation is very hard to do. Communication activities are often under-resourced and given a secondary focus, in favour of more mechanistic aspects of people and change management.

Effective communication is the key to developing alignment and understanding between employers and their employees. Absenteeism cuts to the heart of interpersonal relationships between people and as such, will only be addressed when employers and employees communicate effectively about their respective values, needs and responsibilities. Employer and employee need to understand their respective values relating to the nature and context of work, the business imperatives for the organisation, the demands of work and, for employees the balance between work and the other aspects of their life.

Communication is always most effective and generally preferred at the face-to-face level. However, in most large organisations, in order to deliver consistent messages, an effective communication strategy will involve multiple media. Communication is inherently a two-way street – top down edicts do not constitute communication!

Care must be taken to balance engagement with individuals and teams through direct contact with team leaders and supervisors, with promulgation of wider organisational messages. It is important to design communication approaches to include multiple opportunities for feedback, both directly and confidentially or anonymously. Feedback that is effectively managed and monitored provides a reliable measure of communication effectiveness, as well as informing potential opportunities for improvements.

Building ongoing commitment by employees   6.50

To achieve behaviour change and commitment by employees, it is essential that the organisation clearly states it's expectations in relation to employee attendance, the support provided to assist employees who experience difficulties in fulfilling their obligations, and the consequences for excessive or unjustified absences.

Commencing an effective change programme requires building acceptance of the absence problem and its impact on the organisation and subsequently providing opportunities for employees to contribute to the design of the solution. Gaining a level of acceptance of the requirement to effectively manage absence will generally involve the following processes, namely:

- identification and engagement of key stakeholders;
- developing awareness amongst the target audience(s) about the issue;
- providing information about the new initiatives and proposed changes;
- marketing the concept – what does this mean for the target audience(s);
- implementing and supporting the change; and
- reviewing its effectiveness.

Key stakeholder identification and engagement   6.51

Once it is apparent that absence management is an issue that needs to be addressed, it is advisable to identify and engage interested stakeholders. Stakeholders are defined as those people or groups who have an interest in the issue; who are likely to be impacted by any changes that might occur or who are likely to either support or block the implementation of any proposed changes.

Typical absence management stakeholders within an organisation would be employees, supervisors and managers, and human HR professionals. Other stakeholders who may be important to include are unions and relevant professional associations. Stakeholders are usually engaged through a workplace committee or as individual representatives, who contribute either separately or collectively to the process. It is important to identify potential change 'advocates' and 'blockers' and design different approaches to manage their input and feedback.

Involving stakeholders early in the research is useful, because they are able to provide relevant insights and information to assist the research, interpret the results and validate research findings. In addition, key stakeholders have a vital role in designing the right balance of interventions to address the identified issues and where necessary, can provide valuable championship of the change during its implementation.

Developing awareness amongst the target audiences about the issue   6.52

Effective communication is a key to effective change implementation. At the outset, raising awareness involves providing an accurate account of the existence of an issue in relation to absenteeism and informing stakeholders about the costs, impacts and consequences for the organisation. In so doing, absenteeism becomes a business issue to be managed in order to achieve improved productivity.

Providing early information about a proposed research project to investigate absenteeism in the organisation, allows employees the opportunity to provide feedback on their own experiences and contribute their ideas and suggestions.

Providing information about the new initiatives and proposed changes 6.53

Once a programme to improve absenteeism has been designed and approved, it is important that effort is devoted to making sure that employees understand any changes to their responsibilities. It is also important to provide the opportunity for employees to work through the implications of these changes on their attendance behaviour will assistance in their fulfilment of these obligations.

Resources dedicated to communication will vary depending on the nature of the change and the size and culture of the organisation. Effective communication always involves the delivery of information in multiple forms, reinforcing key messages. This may involve the release of written policies, supported by newsletter publications, email notifications, presentations, team leader briefings and targeted training.

Policy statements must be clear and concise, outlining expectations and obligations in terms of actions and consequences. It is also important to clearly define roles and responsibilities and nominate contact points to enable employees and managers to seek assistance, if they require it.

Marketing the concept 6.54

Key message development is essential to marketing the changes proposed. Key messages are most effective if they are targeted to specific audiences and include clear benefits statements. Benefits are best described to appeal to employees desire to understand 'what's in this for me?'.

All marketing efforts should address the basic messages, which are:

- why are we doing this;
- what are we hoping to achieve;
- what does this mean for each target audience;
- what do the target audience need to do differently; and
- how will we measure the change?

For employees, key messages may relate to individual employee accountability procedures for notifying and explaining absence coupled with advice about the availability of support for mitigating personal circumstances or unresolved workplace issues.

For supervisors, key messages would relate to their responsibilities in developing a healthy and positive workplace culture and their role in motivating employees to improve their attendance and contribution to the organisation. Specific training, coaching and support may need to be provided to enable supervisors to understand and develop effective HR management skills.

Other strategies that may be launched in parallel with the launch of the absence policy may include internal benchmarking and team-based recognition and rewards programmes.

Implementing and supporting change   6.55

Defining an effective start date for the change well in advance will allow employees to prepare and manage the impact on their attendance behaviour dependant on their personal circumstances and their existing working arrangements. There is considerable evidence that the visibility of absence management policies actually affects employee behaviour, resulting in improved attendance.

Implementation of change requires careful planning to ensure that all the required infrastructure and support is in place prior to roll-out.

Copies of policy documents and any supporting forms or online processes, must be in place and operating prior to the commencement date. Any necessary training programmes must be completed. All staff must have a clear understanding of the commencement date and their responsibilities following implementation.

Support strategies must also be in place to deal with consequences associated with the policy. These include availability of HR specialist support staff and EAPs, if relevant.

Building commitment by senior executive   6.56

Developing a business case for improving absence management requires engagement and support of senior management. In order to do this, senior management must be persuaded of the importance of actively managing absenteeism as a *business-critical issue* which is clearly linked to organisational productivity. The business case therefore must be based on both sunk costs and additional costs incurred as a result of indirect consequences related to absenteeism, the potential for improvement either in terms of increased revenue or improved productivity and the potential risks associated with disaffected or unproductive staff.

The HR department has, in a majority of organisations, had a historically low profile in determining business critical issues. An effective HR department provides essential support and assistance to developing a sound business case for change and implementing the resultant policies and support strategies. However, absenteeism is an important issue for the whole business to actively manage and as such requires the attention and active support of senior management across the whole organisation.

Evaluation and Review   6.57

Once the absence change has been implemented, it is important to monitor and review changes in attendance behaviour and adjust the interventions accordingly.

An effective way to manage change is to determine a review date at the commencement of the change initiative to allow the opportunity for adjustments to be made in a managed fashion.

Regular feedback to employees and supervisors about the impact of the change process over time is critical to maintaining focus and momentum. For the audience of general employees, trend data at an organisational as well as business unit or location level is generally sufficient. For managers, measuring attendance within their area of responsibility could provide one important indicator of their management performance.

Routine surveys can provide a useful way of assessing organisational health, providing an effective channel for employees to give feedback and an important lever for the development of a positive workplace culture.

There are numerous survey tools which may be employed, which are usually available from HR consulting companies and peak psychological bodies. Most of these tools can be customised to meet individual requirements. Some organisations choose to create their own surveys.

The following section provides an overview of some types of surveys that are available, which may be of assistance in this area.

Absence management surveys   6.58

Absence management surveys have been developed by a number of HR and recruitment companies. Typically, they are designed to gain greater understanding about what employees use their sick leave for and broadly the types of approaches that employers use to deal with absenteeism.

Team effectiveness surveys   6.59

Team effectiveness surveys are useful for building a sense of shared commitment, through growing understanding of team members' experiences within the group and understanding of shared aspirations.

These surveys can be easily designed and used within small or large teams. They are based on the shared values which the organisation decides relate to promoting a high performance environment. They are generally only between eight and ten questions with multiple-choice or Likert scale responses, for easy analysis. Results can be used to promote discussion about shared values, team working and also to resolve differences of perception.

Health of organisation surveys   6.60

Wellness developmental packages concentrate on the provision of self-development opportunities to build personal wellness management skills including optimal physical, mental and coping skills. Organisational wellness management reports provide a detailed analysis of individual responses and a holistic interpretation of an organisations 'wellness'. Recommended interventions often include team and individual development events focusing on 'well habits'.

> 'The development of these fundamental life skills pays off in terms of greater enjoyment of life as well as higher and more sustainable performance.'

(Anthony Phillips, WellKom Corporate Services.)

Survey uptake is usually high, as employees view the approach as non-stigmatised, proactive and preventive.

Case study 30

WellKom Corporate Services (WCS) developed its Personal, Team and Organisational Wellness Management Profile™ based on the success of NikeTown in Berlin. The recruitment of sports-inspired people led to having in the store people who had exceptional physical and mental well habits as well as highly developed coping strategies. These 'well people' were 'well managed' in terms of all aspects of people management – a high performance culture model proven in international retailing was adapted and implemented. The combination of 'well people' and 'well managed' equals in a 'well organisation'. This is what WCS refers to as wellness management and is reported and developed in the survey tool it has developed. The value of wellness management is demonstrated by the results in Berlin which included a 90 per cent customer retention rate, an average rating for customer experience of 8.7 out of 10 and 35 per cent word of mouth referrals. All in a country where a customer service culture is notoriously difficult to create.

Employee climate surveys   6.61

Employee climate surveys are conducted regularly in many organisations to provide employees with the opportunity to give feedback on their views about the organisation to management. Climate surveys provide organisations with valuable information about employee attitudes, organisational culture and values. Many organisations incorporate climate survey results in their annual reports and managerial performance appraisal systems.

Stress surveys and inventories   6.62

Stress is now the leading cause of sickness absence in the UK. The Health and Safety Executive 2001/2 survey of self-reported work-related illness (SW101/02) prevalence estimate indicated that over half a million individuals in Britain believed that they were experiencing work–related stress at a level that was making them ill. The same study indicated that self-reported stress, anxiety or depression accounts for an estimated 13.5 million reported lost working days per year in Britain.

Employers seeking to manage the significant costs of stress in terms of sickness absence and lost performance are increasingly using 'stress audits' to identify organisational causes of stress that can then be managed through remedial action. One of the UK's leading providers of stress audits, OSA Limited, has been working with blue chip companies and Government departments since 1997. Follow-up audits show that where positive action is taken by employers to tackle the work related causes of stress, stress levels drop and employee well being improves. Stress that originates outside the workplace may be managed through the use of EAPs and other similar support services.

Case study 31

Mature employers now manage stress through action led by a combination of health and safety, OH and HR Departments. OSA has been working globally with a major petroleum company to provide stress audits over a number of years. The company may be regarded as a model employer in terms of its commitment to the pro-active management of stress with support at the highest levels of the company.

In 2003, OSA completed the first global study of stress within a company business unit of 3,500 individuals. The survey was conducted by internet and gave confidential individual feedback to encourage employees to seek help where appropriate. Aggregated data formed the basis of sophisticated management reporting which allowed work and home related issues to be identified by level, department and job function. The leadership team shaped HR, Health and Safety and OH agendas and initiatives based on the stress audit results. Bespoke stress management training was designed for staff at all levels. Based on OSA data and research conducted by Guardian Financial services, it was estimated that the cost of not managing stress within the business unit, in terms of sickness absence and lost performance or productivity, was $7.6 million a year. Managing stress makes sound business sense.

Chapter 7
Prevention is Better than Cure

Introduction   7.1

Often in health and safety practice, it becomes a necessity to deal with ill health and injuries which have arisen during the course of work. However, in a sense, each work-related injury and occupational disease is a failure of the health and safety system. The purpose of health and safety is always to prevent occurrences of disease and injury, although of course, this can never be perfect. An accident will sometimes happen through a chain of events which are unimaginable the first time it occurs. Having happened once should be enough to learn from to prevent any such reoccurrence in the future. Injuries are caused because of human failings, something which will always be present even in the most regulated of systems. Ill health is sometimes caused through ignorance of the health effects of many physical and chemical hazards in common use. Asbestos is a good example of a substance with impressive qualities as an insulator, but not until it had been in use for many years was it realised that it could have such devastating health effects. Health and safety, therefore, strives to reduce the risk of injury and illness to the lowest level reasonably practicable. Modern practice achieves this through a system of assessment of risk and implementation of effective controls to reduce that risk. There is now a comprehensive legal framework which requires risk assessments to be undertaken (competently) and for suitable risk control measures to be put in place and kept under review.

Primary Prevention   7.2

Primary prevention aims to anticipate what harm might arise in any particular circumstance and to put into place measures to stop that harm from occurring. However because we recognise that health and safety can never be perfect the legal framework is based upon the premise of 'so far as is reasonably practicable'. *Section 2(1)* of the *Health and Safety at Work etc. Act 1974 (HSWA 1974)* says 'it shall be the duty of every employer to ensure, *so far as is reasonably practicable*, the health, safety and welfare of all employees. This term had in fact been defined in law in 1949, long before the Health and Safety at Work etc. Act in the case of *Edwards v National Coal Board [1949] 1 AER 743*. Judge Asquith's judgement stated:

> 'Reasonably practicable is a narrower term than "physically possible",
> and seems to me to imply that a computation must be made by the

owner in which the quantum of risk is placed on one scale and the sacrifice involved in the measures necessary for averting the risk (whether in money, time or trouble) is placed on the other, and that if it be shown that there is a gross disproportion between them – the risk being insignificant in relation to the sacrifice – the defendants discharge the onus on them. Moreover, this computation falls to be made by the owner at the time anterior to the accident'.

The judgement formed an important cornerstone to subsequent health and safety law as it set the need to undertake risk assessment. The only way an employer can determine what effort must be made to avert a risk is to have determined the quantity of the risk it has to be balanced against. But from the point of view of prevention, it is the last sentence of the judgement which is important. The risk assessment has to be made at a *time anterior* to the accident, which means it has to be before any accident occurs.

Primary prevention should clearly apply to any circumstances in the workplace, or in the nature of the work being undertaken for which it could reasonably be foreseen that harm might come to the person or persons exposed. The same applies equally to safety issues where physical injury might be envisaged and to factors associated with the work which might reasonably be expected to create a risk of ill health. Successful primary prevention strategies can reduce the risk of injuries and ill health, and for a relatively modest investment in time and resources will significantly reduce the amount of lost time and sickness absence. Primary prevention can be exercised through a number of prevention strategies, undoubtedly the most important being risk assessment.

Prevention Strategies

Risk assessment   7.3

Primary prevention is crucially dependant on risk assessment. There is now a now a legal requirement to assess the risks of any hazard in the workplace. The term 'hazard' applies to anything in the workplace or in the work process that has the *potential* to cause harm. For something to be recognised as a hazard depends on the understanding, knowledge and experience of the person making that judgement. For example, if you did not know that latex gloves had the potential to cause dermatitis, you would not recognise the wearing of latex gloves to be hazard. For this reason, risk assessments have, by law, to be carried out by persons who are competent (see *Regulation 7* of the *Management of Health and Safety at Work Regulations 1999 (SI 1999 No 3242)*). Competency can be defined as having sufficient training, knowledge, experience and other qualities to identify the hazards, to evaluate the risks and to evaluate the effectiveness of the precautions in place to control those risks. The risk assessor does not need to have detailed knowledge of how to devise risk controls, but must be able to have access to the specialist knowledge and information required to propose and implement effective controls. Prevention of occupational ill health, accidents and injury will only succeed if suitable and sufficient controls are put in place to manage the risks. This too is subject to a legal requirement (*SI 1999 No 3242, Reg 5*). The risk assessments required under *SI 1999 No 3242* are those to which no specific regulations apply. Where there is legislation relating to a specific hazard then that takes precedence. For example the potential for harm from exposure to substances at work is subject to risk assessment under the *Control of Substances Hazardous to Health Regulations (COSHH) 2002 (SI 2002 No 2677)*. For Noise at Work, the assessment is done according to the requirements of the *Noise at Work Regulations 1989 (SI 1989 No 1790)* (to be replaced in 2005 by the *Control of Noise at Work Regulations* which implement the EU *Physical Agents (Noise) Directive 2003/10/EU*). Table 4 below lists the hazards for which specific regulations *requiring risk assessment* are in place.

Table 4: Specific regulations requiring risk assessment

Hazard or Risk	*Regulation*
Chemicals, fumes, vapours, dust, microbiological organisms	*Control of Substances Hazardous to Health Regulations (COSHH) 2002 (SI 2002 No 2677)* and *Control of Substances Hazardous to Health (Amendment) Regulations 2003 (SI 2003 No 978).*
Noise	*Noise at Work Regulations 1989 (SI 1989 No 1790)* and EU *Physical Agents (Noise Directive 2003/10/EU)*. Proposed new UK Regulations 2005.
Lifting and carrying of loads	*Manual Handling Operations Regulations 1992 (SI 1992 No 2793)* and *Health and Safety (Miscellaneous Amendments) Regulations 2002, Reg 4 (SI 2002 No 2174).*
Display screen equipment, workstations and work environment	*Health and Safety (Display Screen Equipment) Regulations 1992 (SI 1992 No 2792)* and *Health and Safety (Miscellaneous Amendments) Regulations 2002, Reg 3 (SI 2002 No 2174).*
The use of personal protective equipment	*Personal Protective Equipment at Work Regulations 2002 (SI 2002 No 1144)* as amended by the *Health and Safety (Miscellaneous Amendments) Regulations 2002, Reg 5 (SI 2002 No 2174).*
Fire	*Fire Precautions (Workplace) Regulations 1997 (SI 1997 No 1840)* and *Fire Precautions (Workplace) (Amendment) Regulations 1999 (SI 1999 No 1877).*
Lead	*Control of Lead at Work Regulations 1998 (SI 1998 No 543).*
Asbestos	*Control of Asbestos at Work Regulations 2002 (SI 2002 No 2675).*

Hazard or Risk	Regulation
Ionising radiation	*Ionising Radiations Regulations 1999 (SI 1999 No 3232).*
Genetically modified organisms/genetic manipulation	*Genetically Modified Organisms (Contained Use) Regulations 2000 (SI 2000 No 283)* and *Genetically Modified Organisms (Contained Use) (Amendment) Regulations 2002 (SI 2002 No 63).*
Machinery, work equipment	*Provision and Use of Work Equipment Regulations 1998 (SI 1998 No 2306)* as amended by the *Health and Safety (Miscellaneous Amendments) Regulations 2002, Reg 7 (SI 2002 No 2174).*
Serious and imminent danger and major accidents	*Management of Health and Safety at Work Regulations 1999, Reg 8 (SI 1999 No 3242)* and the *Control of Major Accident Hazards Regulations (COMAH) 1999 (SI 1999 No 743).*
Injuries and sudden illness at work	*Health and Safety (First-Aid) Regulations 1981 (SI 1981 No 917)* and Approved Code of Practice L74 (1999). As amended by the *Management of Health and Safety at Work Regulations 1999, Reg 24 (SI 1999 No 3242)* and the *Health and Safety (Miscellaneous Amendments) Regulations 2002, Reg 2 (SI 2002 No 2174).*
Risks to pregnant women	*Management of Health and Safety at Work Regulations 1999, Reg 16 (SI 1999 No 3242).*
Risks to young workers	*Management of Health and Safety at Work Regulations 1999, Reg 19 (SI 1999 No 3242).*
Other health and safety hazards not covered by specific legislation such as slips, trips and falls, stress, driving, vibration etc	*Management of Health and Safety at Work Regulations 1999 (SI 1999 No 3242).* Note: Vibration will need to be assessed by a new Control of Vibration Regulations which must be introduced by 6 July 2005 to comply with the EU *Physical Agents (Vibration) Directive 2002/44 EC.*

Risk management

7.4

Risk assessment is the first step in the risk control process. The aim of course is not just to identify risks and quantify them, but also to devise and implement plans to avert the risk. This is also a legal requirement under the *Management of Health and Safety at Work Regulations 1999, Regulation 5 (SI 1999 No 3242)* which requires employers to make and give effect to appropriate arrangements for effective planning, organisation, control, and monitoring and review of the preventative and protective measures. *SI 1999 No 3242, Reg 4* requires that any preventative and protective measures which are employed are done so on the basis of the principles laid down in *SI 1999 No 3242, Sch 1* of the Regulations. These principles are:

(a) avoiding risks;

(b) evaluating the risks which cannot be avoided;

(c) combating the risks at source;

(d) adapting the work to the individual;

(e) adapting to technical progress;

(f) replacing the dangerous with the non-dangerous or less dangerous;

(g) developing a coherent overall prevention policy which covers technology, organisation of work, working conditions, social relationships, and the influence of factors relating to the working environment;

(h) giving collective protective measures priority over individual protective measures; and

(i) giving appropriate instructions to employees.

Primary prevention can only be exercised if the risk assessment correctly identifies what the risk are and then develops a risk management strategy which must then be implemented, monitored and reviewed. To be effective in preventing illness and injury, risk assessment can never be a paper exercise. It must be based on a competent assessment of the risks and followed by a pragmatic but effective plan to eliminate them or to manage them to a level which is as low as reasonably practicable.

Pre-employment health assessment   7.5

Pre-employment health assessments are used to ensure that anyone newly employed into a job is *medically fit* to undertake that work. The introduction of the *Disability Discrimination Act 1995 (DDA 1995)* has placed a different emphasis on pre-employment health assessments since it is no longer possible to exclude someone from being employed solely on the basis of a disability that may make it more difficult for that person to undertake the work. A person can no longer be said to be unfit for a job until reasonable adjustments to the work or the workplace have been fully explored.

Pre-employment health assessments therefore now serve four main purposes. They are used to ensure that someone is not recruited to a job for which they are unfit or would be unsafe because of a medical condition, whilst secondly ensuring that the employer complies with his legal duty not to discriminate against prospective employees with a disability. The third function of pre-employment health assessment is to ensure that there is baseline data on medical conditions that the employee may bring to the job (to avoid subsequent claims that it was this employment that caused the condition). Fourthly, a health assessment at the point of recruitment can also ensure that any risks to health in the job are properly controlled. For example if someone is being recruited into a job that exposes them to the risk of hepatitis B then to make sure the necessary vaccinations are given.

The purposes of pre-employment health assessments are therefore to protect the employer from recruiting someone who will be unsafe or unfit for the job and to protect the employee from the known risks associated with the job. It is this last purpose that ensures that primary prevention is exercised.

Pre-employment health checks should ideally be undertaken by a health professional such as an occupational health nurse or doctor. They are usually initially undertaken from a paper-based health declaration completed by the job applicant. Any queries that might arise from the form are followed up by an interview with the nurse or doctor and if necessary taken further by obtaining a medical report from the applicant's doctor. The advice given to managers is then either 'fit', 'fit with certain restrictions', 'unfit' or 'fit subject to certain adjustments being made under *DDA 1995*'. Confidentiality of medical information on employees is important and it is for this reason that the health records are best kept by health professionals.

Vaccinations and immunisations   7.6

In some jobs it is necessary to ensure that employees are protected against the risk of infection. In health care this is a priority, so that the health care worker does not acquire infections from contact with infectious patients and also, with some diseases, does not infect the patient by being a carrier of the disease. This, for example, is the case with hepatitis B, HIV and tuberculosis. With many diseases, it is possible to gain immunity by a programme of vaccinations, but in other cases it is not. There is for example no vaccine against HIV or hepatitis C. Other means of protection including stringent precautions against needle stick injuries and a protocol for treating incidents where injury involving possible blood contact has occurred. Any job in which it is possible to be injured with blood-contaminated needles or other sharp objects, or bitten by potentially infected individuals, will require vaccination against hepatitis B.

Foreign travel also represents a risk of infection and vaccinations should always be brought up to date for employees who are required to travel abroad on business. The precise programme of vaccination (and other protection such a malaria prevention) will depend on where the person is travelling to and to some extent the type of lifestyle they will lead abroad. Expert advice should be obtained from a specialist travel medicine clinic.

Health surveillance   7.7

There is a legal requirement for health surveillance. Some specific Regulations may require health surveillance (such as under *Control of Substances Hazardous to Health Regulations (COSHH) 2002 (SI 2002 No 2677)*, *Control of Asbestos at Work Regulations 2002 (SI 2002 No 2675)*, *Control of Lead at Work Regulations 1998*

(SI 1998 No 543) and *Ionising Radiations Regulations 1999 (SI 1999 No 3232)* –
see table 4 at **7.3** above), and these will usually be specific about what form the
health surveillance should take. Some of these Regulations also require the health
surveillance to be undertaken by an appointed doctor. In the absence of a specific
requirement, *Regulation 6* of the *Management of Health and Safety at Work
Regulations 1999 (SI 1999 No 3242)* requires that:

> 'every employer shall ensure that his employees are provided with such
> heath surveillance as is appropriate having regard to the risks to their
> health and safety which are identified by the assessment.'

The Approved Code of Practice to the Regulations however, qualifies when
health surveillance would be appropriate:

- when there is an identifiable disease or adverse health condition related to
  the work concerned;

- where there are valid techniques available to detect indications of the disease or condition;

- where there is likelihood that the disease or condition may occur under the
  particular conditions of work; and

- where surveillance is likely to further protect the health of the employee.

Health surveillance can form an important part of primary prevention (and indeed
secondary prevention). It tries to ensure that early signs of a disease or adverse
health condition are detected as early as possible so that suitable interventions can
take place to prevent the condition developing or worsening. Health surveillance
can take many forms and it no need to be onerous or expensive for the employer
to undertake. In some cases, it may be necessary to take physiological measurements, such as lung function tests or audiometry (to check on hearing ability), and
in others it may be necessary to periodically measure blood or urine levels of toxic
metals such as beryllium or mercury. These measurements (or blood samples for
analysis), will need to be taken by an occupational health nurse or doctor.
However, the majority of health surveillance is for conditions such a dermatitis or
work-related upper limb disorders which can be undertaken by a competent person but not necessarily by a health professional. A supervisor or some other
responsible person can easily check for signs of dermatitis. In many cases employees can undertake the health surveillance themselves. In the case of upper limb
disorder, for example (which fulfils all of the criteria above for mandatory health
surveillance), employees can be informed about the early signs of upper limb disorder (numbness, tingling, pain) and be encouraged to report any symptoms to
their line manager. If self-surveillance is undertaken without the assistance of a
health professional, it is imperative that the organisation has access to professional
medical advice so that any reported cases can be quickly followed up. A suitable
referral system should be in place before health surveillance is implemented.

Health surveillance is an important procedure for ill health prevention. If a disease
or other adverse health condition is possible from the work or working condi-

tions, early detection of signs and symptoms, and suitable intervention will prevent the condition worsening. This will, in turn, prevent conditions that might otherwise have become chronic from resulting in prolonged sickness absence or even ill health retirement.

Safe systems of work and safe working practices   7.8

Accidents and ill health can be prevented by having in place a safe system of work and adopting safe working practices. Devising a safe system of work normally comes out of the risk assessment. Every aspect of the safe working practice for a particular task or process should be carefully thought through and written down as a set of safety instructions for those involved in that task. For example in a welding workshop the hazards might be determined as burn, fire, inhalation of welding fumes (with a risk of asthma, welders lung or metal fume fever), eye damage from arc welding, harm-arm vibration syndrome from angle grinding, noise and physical injury from handling sheet metal (including manual handing injury and foot injury). A safe system of work therefore needs to be devised to reduce the risk of accidents and ill health in this particular working environment. The safe system of work will involve both engineering solutions, which will reduce the risks of exposure to everyone in the workshop, and personal protection for those risks that cannot adequately be controlled by engineering solutions alone. For example local extract ventilation at the welding torch will reduce fumes significantly in the breathing zone of the welder, and improved ventilation in the workshop as a whole will reduce the exposure of people generally in that area. However, personal protection will have to be provided to prevent the risk of eye damage or foot injury for example. Suitable gloves may have to be provided for grinding using hand tools and ear defenders to reduce the risk of hearing damage. The principle generally is that of giving collective protective measures priority (such as ventilation) over individual protective measures (such as respiratory protective devices), and this principle is contained in *Schedule 1* of the *Management of Health and Safety at Work Regulations 1999 (SI 1999 No 3242)* (see risk management at **7.4** above).

The safe system of work devised for the workshop must be written down in the form of safe working practices (or safe operating procedures). For example, where it is deemed necessary to wear eye protection the type of protection suitable and how and when it should be worn should be stated together with a programme of maintenance and replacement for that particular personal protective equipment (PPE). For ventilation the way it should be used, the maintenance schedule and what to do in the event of equipment failure should be detailed. Each hazard should be addressed in the same way with details of the protective measure to be used, when and how they should be used and how they should be maintained. Most importantly, employees who come within the scope of a safe system of work must be provided with a set of written safety instructions and provided with any instruction and training that may be necessary to ensure that they comply with safety measures in place. (*SI 1999 No 3242, Regs 10* and *13*). *SI 1999 No 3242, Reg 10* requires that the information provide to employees must be 'comprehensible'. This may need special consideration where the employee is dyslexic, has learning difficulties or where English is not the first language. It is good practice to ask employees to sign that they have received *and understand* the safety instructions provided to them. *Section 7* of the *Health and Safety at Work etc. Act 1974* and *SI 1999 No 3242, Reg 14* places a duty on employees to take reasonable care of themselves (and others) and to comply with health and safety instructions and use the safety equipment provided by the employer. It is absolutely essential for prevention to be successful for the employee to comply with the safe system of work devised to protect him or her and to take their own protection seriously.

Developing a safety culture   7.9

A safety culture depends on getting every employee on board with the notion that working to safe systems of work are in their best interests and will prevent illness and injury both to themselves and to their colleagues. Unfortunately, there are many pressures at work that detract from this. Sometimes the protective measures devised interfere with the ability to do the job properly or to socialise and so are ignored or not used properly. Ear defenders will interfere with speech and so are often not used. Eye protection can mist up when it is worn with a face mask and so either the mask or the eye protection is left off. Some heavy protective clothing is very hot and uncomfortable, and so may not be worn. Rest breaks designed to reduce the risk of musculoskeletal injury may be ignored if there are deadlines to meet. Safe lifting limits may be overlooked if there is pressure to complete a task. Protective gloves may reduce the ability to grip or it may just not seem macho to wear them. The list is endless of reasons why people may not use the safety systems devised to prevent illness or injury. In an organisation with a strong safety culture these reasons will be addressed, for example by:

- having a comprehensive safety policy which everyone 'signs up' to;

- having well devised safe systems of working and safe working practices;

- ensuring that all staff are well informed about the risks to their health and safety and what measures have been put in place to protect them; and

- communicating and consulting with staff at all levels to ensure that concerns over the use of safety equipment or safe systems of working are addressed.

A strong safety culture always has to be 'top-down'. Staff who feel that there is a genuine commitment by their managers, senior managers and all the way up to board level, will be much more likely to engage in the collective responsibility for health and safety in the organisation. Evidence for the commitment of senior managers will come, for example, by the safety policy being signed by the chief executive, by a senior manager chairing the health and safety committee (if there is one), and by a genuine understanding of the concerns and problems facing employees when they have health and safety issues. It will not be good enough for managers simply to be sympathetic without having the authority and understanding to be able to try to resolve issues that arise. This authority (and sometimes a budget to support it) will again have to come from the top. Management training is also a key element in developing a good safety culture. Managers need to have an appreciation that health and safety is as important to their business as having people-management skills, technical knowledge or whatever else the business demands of them.

An organisation with a strong health and safety culture will demonstrate a visible presence to health and safety, which everyone is aware of and, most importantly, feels part of. At a simple level this will involve displaying the statutory health and safety information poster in a prominent place (which is a legal requirement under the *Health and Safety Information for Employees Regulations 1989 (SI 1989 No 682)*), but will also have other health and safety information (leaflets and posters) displayed in prominent places. The health and safety policy statement will be displayed where people frequently see it. Many organisations also open themselves to external audit and obtain a visible recognition of health and safety best practice by obtaining and displaying one of the recognised awards such as the British Safety Council 5 Star Award or the RoSPA Health and Safety Performance Rating (HSPR).

All of these visible commitments to health and safety must be supported by good communication on health and safety matters within the organisation. Where there is no union health and safety representative system in place then, by law, organisations have to elect 'Representatives of Employee Safety' under the *Health and Safety (Consultation With Employees) Regulations 1996 (SI 1996 No 1513)*. The purpose of health and safety representatives is to act as a conduit for the two-way flow of information on health and safety issues between management and the group of employees they represent. In an organisation with a good safety culture, the role of health and safety representatives is seen by both employees and employers as making an important and valuable contribution to health and safety performance. Unfortunately in some organisations the representative role is a confrontational one in which managers resent what they see as interference in the way they run their business and employees use health and safety issues to score points with management. The intended safety culture is turned in to a blame culture. It is essential in developing a strong health and safety culture that communication on health and safety is seen by management as a positive way of improving their business and by employees as a way of preventing illness and injury.

Organisations with a good health and safety culture are likely to be more successful businesses to the advantage of both the organisation and their employees. Their success in preventing illness and injury will be reflected in lower rates of accidents and sickness absence. The HSC's Model for Continuous Improvement in Occupational Health and Safety Culture, identifies three types of organisation. The uninterested, the complier and the very good. The uninterested organisation will be driven, if at all, by enforcement, regulations, insurance and costs of non-compliance. The complier will be driven by these same legislative requirements, but will have some humanitarian concerns for employees and will fear the embarrassment of 'being caught'. The very good, by contrast, will usually not be driven primarily by enforcement and regulation but the prime motivator in these organisations is concern for their employees, seeing health and safety as an investment for the future (rather than as a cost for today), a desire to be excellent and corporate social responsibility. It is these features of a organisation which single them out as having a strong health and safety culture. The HSC's model provides suggestions as to how organisations can progress from one category to the next (see: www.ohstrategy.net).

Preventing Non-Work Related Illness and Injury

Good health is good business   7.10

The HSE slogan 'Good Health is Good Business' is an apt way of emphasising that employers should be concerned for the health of their employees. The biggest asset for any organisation is its staff and it makes very good business sense to protect that vital asset. There is a very strong legal framework for employers to protect the work-related health of their employees, and there may be severe financial penalties in the civil courts if they fail in their duty of care to their employees whilst they are at work. Helping to prevent illness and injury whilst outside of work is therefore an altruistic action on the part of the employer. The benefits of this to the organisation often have to be taken on trust since it is often not possible to clearly demonstrate how many instances of illness and accident have been prevented by promoting health and a healthy lifestyle. Even looking at rates of sickness and injury before and after the introduction of health promotion programmes fails to demonstrate clear benefits because these are often long term. Programmes which help people choose a healthier diet, lose weight or stop smoking will take decades to show that they have reduced the incidence of cancer, diabetes, or heart disease. However, there are many epidemiological studies to show that adopting a healthier lifestyle does have significant benefits in reducing the risk of serious illness later in life. There is no doubt about the value of such programmes to the individual, but the employer may not reap the benefits within the period of time that person is an employee.

The benefits to the organisation are therefore real but less clearly linked to reductions in short-term sickness or lost-time injury. Encouraging employees to stop smoking, to lose weight, to be aware of cancer risks etc will reduce the risk of long-term employees having serious illness which necessitates them having prolonged sickness absence or taking medical retirement. Sometimes, however, the benefits may accrue to other employers who employ those staff later in their lives. However, the public health benefits to the country as a whole from using the workplace as a venue for encouraging healthy living is considered by the Government as being significant. The Government's Occupational Health Strategy for England, Wales and Scotland (Securing Health Together), emphasises the importance of the workplace as a venue for promoting a healthy lifestyle. Employers who engage in health education and health promotion in the workplace will be investing in improving the nation's health, and will therefore be indirectly investing in their own future.

The immediate benefits of a health promotion programme in the workplace come from having a workforce that feels valued. Whilst the health benefits may take time to accrue, the benefits in terms of people feeling that the organisation cares about them and values them will be more immediate. Some health promotion initiatives such as providing in-house gym facilities, subsidising private gym membership or providing exercise classes can have more short term tangible benefits by improving staff fitness.

Health promotion   7.11

Health promotion in the workplace is a commitment by the employer to improving the health of their workforce. As discussed above, it may not represent an immediate payback in reduced sickness but it will help to ensure that employees can make healthy choices, will make staff feel valued and will improve staff morale. In the longer term, and in public health terms, improved staff health will reduce sickness absence and staff turnover, especially for serious debilitating diseases such as stroke, heart disease and cancer. More immediate benefits may come from improvements in physical fitness, reduced stress levels and reductions in obesity.

Health promotion involves providing information on relevant health issues, increasing awareness of disease risk factors, providing information on healthier alternatives and encouraging self-help. Information can be imparted by leaflets and booklets, but in isolation these sometimes have limited impact. It is better, if possible, to have health promotion initiatives provided by a health promotion specialist or occupational health advisor. These initiatives can take the form of lunch-time seminars, small group sessions on selected topics, or theme days such as healthy heart days or healthy eating days. Good organisations will supplement the information provision with policies and practices which demonstrate their commitment to a healthy workplace. These might include a no-smoking policy at work, a stress policy and stress management training, driving policy or healthy food options in the staff canteen, or provision or subsidy of fitness programmes.

Health promotion topics include the following, although this should not be taken as an exhaustive list of the possibilities for promoting health.

- **Sexual health**. There is a growing concern about the sexual health especially of young people. Unplanned pregnancies and sexually transmitted diseases are a growing concern for the health of the young employee.

- **Tobacco**. In the UK, smoking kills 120,000 people every year and a vastly greater number of smoking-related illness. About 25 per cent of the workforce will be smokers, with a slightly greater number of females now smoking than males. Health promotion on smoking may take the form of educating people, especially young people not to smoke (although the majority will have taken up the habit before leaving school) and providing practical advice and support in giving up smoking. Employers can encourage this by having a smoking ban or smoking restrictions in the workplace.

- **Nutrition**. Good nutrition is vital in promoting good health and preventing disease. A good diet helps to prevent some forms of cancer, and heart and blood vessel disease. It helps control other health problems common in modern society such as obesity, diabetes and oral disease. Health promotion at work can help employees understand the principles of healthy eating and give them the information to make informed choices when buying and cooking food and eating out. The organisation can reinforce the healthy eating message by only serving healthy food options in the staff canteen.

- **Physical activity**. The majority of adults in the UK do not engage in the levels of activity necessary to benefit their health. Inactivity is recognised as a major contributor to the risk of coronary heart disease, and can increases the risk of colon cancer, diabetes, hypertension (high blood pressure) and obesity. Increased physical activity can improve the immune system, reducing the risk of common infectious illnesses and promotes psychological well-being. All of these factors can make a significant impact on employee performance. Health promotion at work should aim to encourage staff to take up a reasonable level of physical activity. This might be further encouraged by sponsoring membership of gyms or exercise groups or even, in larger organisations, providing in-house facilities. Organisations in which the work is largely static, have a greater responsibility to encourage physical activity.

- **Weight control**. Obesity is seen as a modern health epidemic. Obesity is linked with a greatly increased risk of heart disease, diabetes and premature death. It is linked in many cases to lack of exercise and poor nutrition. As well as including these in a general approach to health promotion at work, it may be important also to include special support for those who wish to lose weight by a supervised programme of diet and exercise.

- **Mental health**. Mental health issues such as depression and stress are becoming a major health issue affecting many peoples' lives and impacting severely on the employer. Health promotion activities in the workplace can help employees understand and manage those events in their lives, including those at work, which adversely affect their mental health.

- **Drugs and solvents**. Drug and solvent abuse is an important public health issue. Substance abuse can have major impact on health and safety and in some safety-critical jobs it may be necessary to have a policy of drug testing. However, substance abuse is a complex and specialised area. Preventing drug abuse is probably only successful if tackled at an age long before starting work. In the workplace therefore it often a matter of helping those who already have a drug problem and need help. This can only be undertaken by specialists who have experience in this field of work. The employer may need to find a suitably experienced agency to help deal with drug and solvent abuse issues at work.

Health screening 7.12

Health screening refers to a series of tests which the employee can have taken in the workplace to detect early signs of disease. Most of these tests are available on the NHS through a GP, but often they have to be asked for and sometimes GP's are reluctant to undertake them on demand. Many employers therefore provide health screening on the basis that it is an important contributor to health promotion and the prevention of illness and, if it is provided at work, it ensures that everyone has easy access to the screening. It can of course only be voluntary.

Health screening varies widely. It usually includes tests for cardiac risk factors (such as blood cholesterol and low density lipoproteins), blood pressure, urine test for diabetes, tests for colon cancer and prostate cancer. It sometimes also includes a blood sample from which routine measures of blood cell count and biochemical data can give an indication of any abnormalities. The health screening also usually includes measures of height and weight from which body mass ratio can be calculated and compared with normal values. This can give employees a guide to their ideal weight and possibly the need to lose weight. Health screening programmes can also include well women screening including cervical smears and breast cancer screening but these are now readily available on the national health service and today rarely form part of occupational health screening programmes. A good health screening programme should also include an opportunity for staff to be interviewed by the occupational health nurse (who usually administers the screening programme). It gives staff the opportunity to raise questions or concerns they may have about their health and it gives the occupational health nurse an opportunity to ask questions that may give a clue to the individual's mental health. Clues such as sleeplessness, tearfulness, frequent headaches or low self-esteem can often be a clue to depression or stress.

Health screening can also be linked to occupational health requirements such as vision screening required under the *Health and Safety (Display Screen Equipment) Regulations 1992 (SI 1992 No 2792)* or routine hearing or lung function tests or blood tests for exposure to toxic chemicals. It is important wherever it is necessary to do so to include the tests for occupational health purposes within the programme for general lifestyle screening.

Secondary Prevention   7.13

Secondary prevention aims to prevent the reoccurrence or exacerbation of disease or injury when a person returns to work from a period of absence for a cause which is known to the employer. For example if someone has been off sick from a back injury, whether or not it was caused by work, then the employer has a duty to ensure so far as is reasonably practical, that the back injury is not made worse by work when the person returns. This applies to any condition which the employer is aware of and which might be made worse by the conditions of work when the person returns. Stress, heart disease, stroke, injuries to the upper limb, abdominal operations (which might give rise to a risk of injury when lifting), are some of the reasons which might give rise to the need to re-evaluate the work when a person returns following sickness absence. It may be the case that restrictions to prevent a reoccurrence are temporary if the person is fit to return to work but nevertheless still recovering. The period of extra care may therefore be short, but in other cases the vulnerability will be permanent and long-term re-adjustments may have to be made.

Revisiting the risk assessment   7.14

It is important to revisit any risk assessments which apply to the individual return-ing to work. The risk assessment may come to a different conclusion if the person involved now has a condition which did not apply when it was first undertaken. For example someone returning to a electronics engineer's job, following the fit-ting of a cardiac pacemaker, will need to be reassessed to make sure that the pace-maker is not interferred with by the electromagnetic radiation to which the person is exposed. What was a low-risk environment before the persons' illness has now become a moderately high-risk environment.

The employer's extra duty of care   7.15

The common law concept of extra duty of care, and case law from which it was derived, was discussed in **CHAPTER 2**. Where an employer has knowledge of an employee's vulnerability then he owes that person a duty of care over and above that defined by a normal duty of care. This concept is critical in ensuring that measures for secondary prevention are put in place when someone returns to work following a period of sickness absence. The reason for this is that the employer cannot argue that they did not know of a person's vulnerability as they will almost certainly have knowledge of the reason for the employee's absence. The courts will apply a test of reasonable forseeability. Was it foreseeable that a person returning to work following a period of sick leave was more vulnerable than before he was sick? Since the reason for the sickness will have been docu-mented in the sick notes provided by the employee's doctor it would be difficult for the employer to argue that they did not know of the reasons for the person's sickness absence. However, the reason for the sickness absence alone may not provide sufficient cause to foresee that the person will be more at risk. For exam-ple a fork-lift truck driver returning to work following an eye injury may be per-fectly fit to return to work if recovery is complete and there is no resulting impairment of vision. However, if the injury has resulted in a serious impairment of vision then they may be returning to work at considerably greater risk to themself and others with whom they work. If there is any suspicion or uncer-tainty that an employee returning to work may be more prone to illness or injury, or may be putting others at risk, then a medical opinion should be sought either from the employee's GP or by referral to the occupational health department.

In some cases, and stress is a classic example, it must automatically be assumed that a person returning to work may be more vulnerable. The case of *Walker v Northumberland County Council [1995] 1 All ER 737* and the more recent case of *Barber v Somerset County Council [2004] UKHL 13 HL(E)* show clearly that the courts will agree that a documented period of sickness absence for stress must be taken by the employer as evidence of that person's proneness to stress (see **CHAPTER 2**). The employer then has an extra duty of care to ensure that the per-son's stress is not made worse by the return to work. The employer must make reasonable adjustments to the work itself, to the work environment or the hours of work so that the person is less likely to be stressed by work. If work was, or appears to have been, the reason for the stress then the employer has a greater duty, because avoiding a recurrence of the circumstances that led to the stress is within the employer's control. However, even if the stress was not caused by work the employer still has a duty to ensure that the person's condition is not worsened by work. Other examples in which a vulnerability must be assumed is sick leave for an upper-limb disorder where the work involves repetitive upper limb activity, or back pain or back injury where the work involves lifting and carrying.

The implications of the Disability Discrimination Act 1995
7.16

The *Disability Discrimination Act 1995* (*DDA 1995*) is fully discussed in **CHAPTER 4** and the role of the occupational health department in its implementation is discussed in **CHAPTER 2**. It is not the purpose here to explain the Act in any more detail, but simply to emphasise its importance in the process of secondary prevention. A person returning to work after a period of sickness may return to work with a disability that was not apparent before the absence. The civil duty of ensuring that the person is not made worse by the conditions of work is explained at **7.15** above. In addition to that responsibility, the employer has a statutory obligation under *DDA 1995* to ensure that the person with a disability is not put at a disadvantage compared to someone without that disability. The definition of disability is quite wide under the Act which includes both mental and physical disabilities, but to be a disability under the Act the impairment must be both substantial and have long-term adverse effect on ability to carry out day-to-day activities. A medical opinion from the occupational health department or the employee's doctor will usually have to be obtained to determine if the disability falls within the meaning of the Act. If it does, then reasonable adjustments will have to be made to the work or work environment to ensure that the employee is not disadvantaged.

The role of occupational health in secondary prevention
7.17

The role of the occupational health department in rehabilitation generally is explained in **CHAPTER 2**. Secondary prevention is an essential part of the rehabilitation process. It ensures not only that a person returns successfully to work after a period of sickness absence, but in addition tries to reduce the risk of factors associated with the work causing a reoccurrence or exacerbation of the person's condition. The occupational health department plays an important part in both the rehabilitation process (see **CHAPTER 2**) and advising on secondary prevention. The occupational health advisor or occupational health physician will have a detailed understanding of the person's medical condition and can advise the organisation on the likely factors in the work which might cause a worsening or reoccurrence of the illness or injury. The occupational health team can also make an important contribution to the revised risk assessment. In addition the occupational health department (including perhaps input from occupational hygienists and ergonomists) can also make an important contribution to determining what adjustments will be necessary under the *Disability Discrimination Act 1995 (DDA 1995)* to accommodate any newly acquired disability. The occupational health doctor or nurse will also be able to advise the organisation, usually after receiving reports from the person's treating doctors, what the prognosis of the person's condition is, and whether it falls within the definition of disability under *DDA 1995*.

Conclusion   7.18

There are many ways in which diseases and injuries resulting from work can be prevented. Having a good grasp of the hazards and associated risks and reducing those risks to a low level is not only a legal obligation, but absolutely essential in preventing people becoming ill or injured as result of their work. Keeping people under close health surveillance if the risks suggest that an identified illness can be detected early can also play an important role in preventing progression of work-related illness. However, occupational health is not just about preventing and dealing with illnesses caused by work, it also about promoting good health and ensuring that people are fit to undertake the work for which they are engaged. Pre-employment or pre-placement health screening attempts to assure the employing organisation that people recruited to a job are medically fit for the work that is intended of them. Health promotion activities in the workplace are an attempt to persuade employees to adopt healthy lifestyles that will reduce their risk of chronic, debilitating and life-threatening diseases and increase their levels of physical fitness and well-being.

Whilst the very best of prevention practices will reduce the risks of illness and injury it will never eliminate them and the employer has little control over events which cause illness and injury outside of work. Rehabilitation aims to ensure that employees who have been ill or injured, for whatever reason, are successfully returned to work. As part of the rehabilitation process, secondary prevention aims to ensure that when returning to work, an employee will not be exposed to the same risks that caused the condition. If they return to work with a newly acquired vulnerability or disability then secondary prevention aims to ensure that this does not further increase the risks of disease or injury.

Whilst no-one doubts that prevention is better than cure, prevention can never be perfect. There will always be need for rehabilitating the sick or injured employee.

Index

References are to paragraph numbers.